THE PEALE FAMILY

THE PEALE FAMILY

Three Generations of American Artists

Organized by

CHARLES H. ELAM

Sponsored by

FOUNDERS SOCIETY DETROIT INSTITUTE OF ARTS

and

MUNSON-WILLIAMS-PROCTOR INSTITUTE

UTICA, NEW YORK

THE DETROIT INSTITUTE OF ARTS

and

WAYNE STATE UNIVERSITY PRESS

1967

FRONTISPIECE

2 *THE ARTIST IN HIS MUSEUM (detail)*

by Charles Willson Peale

The Pennsylvania Academy of the Fine Arts

DESIGNED BY WILLIAM A. BOSTICK

COMPOSED IN CASLON TYPES BY ARNOLD-POWERS, INC., DETROIT, MICHIGAN

PRINTED IN THE UNITED STATES OF AMERICA BY LITHO-ART, INC., MADISON HEIGHTS, MICHIGAN

CONTENTS

PREFACE

The early rise and flourishing of the Peale family for more than a hundred years was one of the most remarkable phenomena of the American scene. "Painting was the cottage industry, and the Peales produced more artists than the Adams family did statesmen, or the Beechers preachers," Oliver Jensen has observed in *American Heritage*.

The purpose of this exhibition is to trace in its variety the multitudinous character of the work of this family which started about two hundred years ago with Charles Willson Peale and extended through three generations until about one hundred years ago. For two generations the family furnished highly competent and sometimes delightful professional artists, though scarcely any equalled the fire, enthusiasm and originality of the founder of the dynasty, who consequently receives the greatest representation in the exhibition. With few exceptions artist members of the third and subsequent generations of the Peale family were amateurs.

The authors of the introductory articles in this book formed an informal consulting committee. Thanks to them and to the lenders of the objects of art listed herewith, it was possible to present this work. Many other persons offered assistance and helpful suggestions, and we cite especially one made by David H. Wallace that the first and last portraits painted by Charles Willson Peale for the "Gallery of Distinguished Personages" in Peale's Philadelphia Museum should be included in the selection from the Independence National Historical Park collection under his care (no. 34 and 40).

The exhibition is scheduled to be shown at the Detroit Institute of Arts from January 18 through March 5 and at the Munson-Williams-Proctor Institute, Utica, New York, from March 28 through May 7, 1967. William A. Bostick designed this book and Charles H. Elam made the final selection and compiled the entries for the catalog.

WILLIS F. WOODS, *Director*
The Detroit Institute of Arts

28 BENJAMIN FRANKLIN
by Charles Willson Peale
The Historical Society of Pennsylvania

LIST OF LENDERS

Amherst College, Amherst, Massachusetts—no. 6, 122, 140

Addison Gallery of American Art, Phillips Academy, Andover, Massachusetts—no. 73, 170

The University of Michigan Museum of Art, Ann Arbor, Michigan—no. 161

Maryland Historical Society, Baltimore, Maryland —no. 61, 116, 189, 196, 217, 218

The Trustees of the Municipal Museum of Baltimore Inc., The Peale Museum, Baltimore, Maryland— no. 4, 152, 164, 215

Walters Art Gallery, Baltimore, Maryland—no. 154, 192

Museum of Fine Arts, Boston, Massachusetts—no. 14, 56, 115, 149, 169, 178

The Brooklyn Museum, Brooklyn, New York— no. 126

Robert Carlen, Philadelphia, Pennsylvania—no. 224

Carolina Art Association, Gibbes Art Gallery, Charleston, South Carolina—no. 145

The Art Institute of Chicago, Chicago, Illinois—no. 42, 76, 88, 181

Cincinnati Art Museum, Cincinnati, Ohio—no. 16, 17, 102

The Cleveland Museum of Art, Cleveland, Ohio— no. 52

David David Inc., Philadelphia, Pennsylvania—no. 142

The Dayton Art Institute, Dayton, Ohio—no. 200

The Henry Ford Museum, Dearborn, Michigan—no. 27, 108, 109, 193, 194

The Detroit Institute of Arts, Detroit, Michigan— no. 7, 43, 66, 69, 70, 110, 111, 134-36, 157, 167, 175, 177, 186, 209

James Graham and Sons Inc., New York, N. Y.— no. 159

Washington County Museum of Fine Arts, Hagerstown, Maryland—no. 101, 151

Dr. and Mrs. Lysle N. Harrington, Barneveld, N. Y. —no. 13

Mr. and Mrs. F. Palmer Hart, Red Hook, N. Y.— no. 141

Wadsworth Atheneum, Hartford, Connecticut—no. 106, 132

Art Association of Indianapolis, Herron Museum of Art, Indianapolis, Indiana—no. 83

Insurance Company of North America, Philadelphia, Pennsylvania—no. 78

Nelson Gallery and Atkins Museum, Kansas City, Missouri—no. 113, 114, 124

Kennedy Galleries Inc., New York, N. Y.—no. 125, 137, 176, 223

Dr. and Mrs. Irving Levitt, Southfield, Michigan— no. 79, 211

Washington and Lee University, Lexington, Virginia —no. 35, 155

The J. B. Speed Art Museum, Louisville, Kentucky —no. 84

Mr. and Mrs. Harold O. Love, Grosse Pointe Shores, Michigan—no. 203

J. William Middendorf II, New York, N. Y.—no. 5, 8, 53

Milwaukee Art Center, Milwaukee, Wisconsin—no. 118, 171

Walker Art Center, Minneapolis, Minnesota—no. 165

The Newark Museum, Newark, New Jersey—no. 105, 198, 199, 213

Yale University Art Gallery, New Haven, Connecticut—no. 21, 57, 77, 117, 190

Lyman Allyn Museum, New London, Connecticut —no. 168

The American Museum of Natural History, New York, N. Y.—no. 201, 210

The Metropolitan Museum of Art, New York, N. Y. —no. 36, 51, 54, 58, 143

The New-York Historical Society, New York, N. Y. —no. 3, 26

Norfolk Museum of Arts and Sciences, Norfolk, Virginia—no. 212

Mr. and Mrs. William L. Page, New Castle, New Hampshire—no. 11

James Ogelsby Peale, Mountainville, New Jersey— no. 180, 195, 221

The Academy of Natural Sciences of Philadelphia, Philadelphia, Pennsylvania—no. 38

American Philosophical Society Library, Philadelphia, Pennsylvania—no. 1, 64, 99, 100, 163, 202, 204-8

The Historical Society of Pennsylvania, Philadelphia, Pennsylvania—no. 15, 22, 28, 50, 62, 129, 138, 156, 188

Independence National Historical Park, Philadelphia, Pennsylvania—no. 18, 20, 25, 30, 33, 34, 39, 40, 47, 59

The Pennsylvania Academy of the Fine Arts, Philadelphia, Pennsylvania—no. 2, 72, 74, 128, 197, 216

Commissioners of Fairmount Park, courtesy of the Philadelphia Museum of Art, Philadelphia, Pennsylvania—no. 10

Museum of Art, Carnegie Institute, Pittsburgh, Pennsylvania—no. 19, 29, 46, 48, 49, 81, 82, 123, 162

William J. Poplack, Birmingham, Michigan—no. 174, 225

Private Collections—no. 60, 65, 107

The Reading Public Museum and Art Gallery, Reading, Pennsylvania—no. 130

Miss Page Robinson, Chicago, Illinois—no. 12

M. H. de Young Memorial Museum, San Francisco, California—no. 103

Santa Barbara Museum of Art, Santa Barbara, California—no. 91, 92

Dr. and Mrs. Charles Coleman Sellers, Carlisle, Pennsylvania—no. 9, 45, 63, 67, 68, 75, 94, 144, 166, 173, 187, 214, 219, 220

The R. W. Norton Art Gallery, Shreveport, Louisiana—no. 71, 86, 89, 90, 93, 95, 120, 121, 146, 183-85, 191

Mr. and Mrs. Walter E. Simmons, Grosse Pointe Farms, Michigan—no. 55

The Parrish Art Museum, Southampton, N. Y.— no. 179

Museum of Fine Arts, Springfield, Massachusetts— no. 133

The Toledo Museum of Art, Toledo, Ohio—no. 150

Munson-Williams-Proctor Institute, Utica, N. Y.— no. 96, 127, 131, 172

The Corcoran Gallery of Art, Washington, D. C.— no. 104

Library of Congress, Washington, D. C.—no. 148, 158, 160, 222

National Collection of Fine Arts, Smithsonian Institution, Washington, D. C.—no. 80, 85, 87, 112, 119

National Gallery of Art, Washington, D. C.—no. 37, 147, 153

National Portrait Gallery, Smithsonian Institution, Washington, D. C.—no. 32, 41

United States National Museum, Smithsonian Institution, Washington, D. C.—no. 23, 24

Arthur Whallon, Centerville, Indiana—no. 182

Colonial Williamsburg, Williamsburg, Virginia—no. 31, 97, 98

Mrs. Norman B. Woolworth, New York, N. Y.— no. 139

Worcester Art Museum, Worcester, Massachusetts —no. 44

Partial Genealogy of the First Three American Generations of the Peale Family

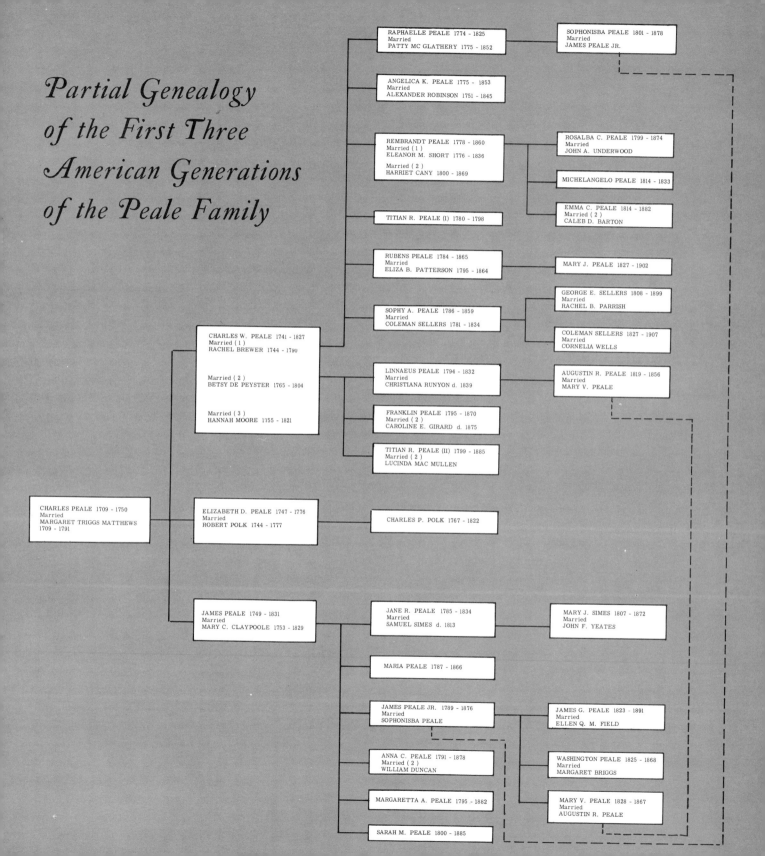

RAPHAELLE PEALE 1774 - 1825
Married
PATTY MC GLATHERY 1775 - 1852

SOPHONISBA PEALE 1801 - 1878
Married
JAMES PEALE JR.

ANGELICA K. PEALE 1775 - 1853
Married
ALEXANDER ROBINSON 1751 - 1845

REMBRANDT PEALE 1778 - 1860
Married (1)
ELEANOR M. SHORT 1776 - 1836
Married (2)
HARRIET CANY 1800 - 1869

ROSALBA C. PEALE 1799 - 1874
Married
JOHN A. UNDERWOOD

MICHELANGELO PEALE 1814 - 1833

EMMA C. PEALE 1814 - 1882
Married (2)
CALEB D. BARTON

TITIAN R. PEALE (I) 1780 - 1798

RUBENS PEALE 1784 - 1865
Married
ELIZA B. PATTERSON 1795 - 1864

MARY J. PEALE 1827 - 1902

SOPHY A. PEALE 1786 - 1859
Married
COLEMAN SELLERS 1781 - 1834

GEORGE E. SELLERS 1808 - 1899
Married
RACHEL B. PARRISH

COLEMAN SELLERS 1827 - 1907
Married
CORNELIA WELLS

CHARLES W. PEALE 1741 - 1827
Married (1)
RACHEL BREWER 1744 - 1790
Married (2)
BETSY DE PEYSTER 1765 - 1804
Married (3)
HANNAH MOORE 1755 - 1821

LINNAEUS PEALE 1794 - 1832
Married
CHRISTIANA RUNYON d. 1839

AUGUSTIN R. PEALE 1819 - 1856
Married
MARY V. PEALE

FRANKLIN PEALE 1795 - 1870
Married (2)
CAROLINE E. GIRARD d. 1875

TITIAN R. PEALE (II) 1799 - 1885
Married (2)
LUCINDA MAC MULLEN

CHARLES PEALE 1709 - 1750
Married
MARGARET TRIGGS MATTHEWS
1709 - 1791

ELIZABETH D. PEALE 1747 - 1776
Married
ROBERT POLK 1744 - 1777

CHARLES P. POLK 1767 - 1822

JAMES PEALE 1749 - 1831
Married
MARY C. CLAYPOOLE 1753 - 1829

JANE R. PEALE 1785 - 1834
Married
SAMUEL SIMES d. 1813

MARY J. SIMES 1807 - 1872
Married
JOHN F. YEATES

MARIA PEALE 1787 - 1866

JAMES PEALE JR. 1789 - 1876
Married
SOPHONISBA PEALE

JAMES G. PEALE 1823 - 1891
Married
ELLEN Q. M. FIELD

ANNA C. PEALE 1791 - 1878
Married (2)
WILLIAM DUNCAN

WASHINGTON PEALE 1825 - 1868
Married
MARGARET BRIGGS

MARGARETTA A. PEALE 1795 - 1882

MARY V. PEALE 1828 - 1867
Married
AUGUSTIN R. PEALE

SARAH M. PEALE 1800 - 1885

INTRODUCTION

Two hundred years ago Charles Willson Peale was studying art in London in the studio of Benjamin West. Young Peale was not a novice and had already established a reputation as a portrait painter in his native American colonies, yet of course the training in London resulted in his artistic maturity. He absorbed West's "classically mannered and highly finished style" and his credo that to produce historical pieces was the highest achievement an artist could attain. The earliest work presented here is a copy by Charles Willson Peale of one of West's

"moral historical pieces" (no. 68), exactly two hundred years old.

In the *History of the Rise and Progress of the Arts of Design in the United States* (New York 1834), William Dunlap quoted from a published memoir by Rembrandt Peale about his father as follows: "The writer of this article was informed by Colonel Trumbull, that one day when he was in Mr. West's painting-room, some hammering arrested his attention. 'Oh,' said Mr. West, 'that is only that ingenious young Mr. Peale, repairing some of my bells and locks.'" Although he took pains to disprove this story by showing that Peale and Trumbull were not in London at the same time, Dunlap did not disprove the "ring of truth" in West's remark (which might well have been made to someone else) and even substantiated it as he continued:

Mr. Leslie, in one of his letters from West Point, says, "Charles Willson Peale, Rembrandt's father, was a pupil of West's. Mr. West painted to the last with a palette, which Peale had most ingeniously mended for him, after he (West) had broken and thrown it aside as useless. It was a small palette; but he never used any other for his largest pictures." This is an anecdote showing the gratitude of the pupil, and the regard which his illustrious master had for his memory.

Mr. Peale, who seems to have wished to play every part in life's drama, not content with being a saddler, a coach-maker, a clock and watch-maker, a silver-smith, and a portrait-painter, studied while in London modelling in wax, moulding and casting in plaster, painting in miniature, and engraving in mezzotinto. These were studies allied to painting.

The "engraving in mezzotinto" of *Mr.*

Pitt (no. 45), printed by Peale in London, to our modern eyes is an amusing potpourri of all the notions of the "grand tradition" and "classical refinement" current in England at the time. It is, nonetheless, an amazing example of the artist's craftsmanship and probably the most technically accomplished engraving produced by an American-born artist up to its time. Its lack of success led Peale to suspect that he was not destined to be a history painter. It was just as well. There was no demand for "history" in America but, in an age before the invention of photography, there was a demand for portraitists. As Dunlap wrote, on Peale's return to Annapolis in 1769

> he found constant employment at portrait-painting. He was now probably the only portrait-painter in that region. Mr. Peale, having brothers and sisters, made them all painters. His brother James became a respectable miniature painter.

Anyone who writes about Charles Willson Peale is necessarily indebted to the comprehensive and scholarly researches of Charles Coleman Sellers, a descendant of Charles Willson Peale. His two-volume biography (Philadelphia 1947) is sound, sympathetic (which Dunlap was not), and eminently readable—a constant delight—and his *Portraits and Miniatures by Charles Willson Peale* (Philadelphia 1952) not only lists 1046 portraits and miniatures, locating many of them and characterizing most sitters (a supplement is in preparation to make it a complete record of the art of Charles Willson Peale), but also has introductory notes placing the artist's production in the tradition of eighteenth century portraiture and discussing his philosophy and techniques. Dr. Sellers has graciously written about the art of Charles Willson Peale and his brother James for this catalog.

Until Peale's Museum was well established in Philadelphia early in the nineteenth century, the production of portraits was the mainstay of the family, and of many of its members even thereafter. Portraits fall into several distinct categories, the largest, perhaps, being those made on com-

mission for the sitter or his family. Frequently these contain accessories pertaining to the subject's profession or occupation, and Peale painted his sitters with an "easy intimate grace," befitting both his own temperament and the "Age of Reason."

"Portraits of public men for public buildings," Charles Coleman Sellers further observed, "still required the old standing pose, with the air and gesture of nobility, in the style of Copley's *Samuel Adams*, his *John Adams*, or Stuart's *Lansdowne Washington*. Peale, in contrast to these, could never paint that air of stern command; let custom demand it or no, all his formal fulllengths, the best of which is his official *Washington* of 1779 (cf. no. 52), are all at

53

52

ease, affable, welcoming, agreeably amused. Even his enormously conventional *William Pitt* of 1769 (cf. no. 45), painted from a bust of the subject, stands before Liberty's altar, with the Magna Carta in his hand, with symbols of the death of tyrants all around him, but smiling in the bland, good-humored assurance that all will be well at the last."

A special category in the Peale *oeuvre* is related to both the privately commissioned and the public portrait. These are the portraits made for "The Gallery of Distinguished Personages" in Peale's Philadelphia Museum. They are a standard 23 x 19 inches in size, usually with unfinished corners, to be matted oval. At first those in the museum were original life portraits or replicas by Charles Willson Peale himself (or James), but for their abortive museum venture in Baltimore in 1797, his sons Raphaelle and Rembrandt made copies of all of them. Later, after the elder Peale retired around the turn of the century from accepting commissions for portraits, Raphaelle and Rembrandt were subsidized, so to speak, to paint portraits of celebrated "personages" from life to bring the "gallery" up-to-date. These in turn were copied by other members of the second generation. Many of these copies, and earlier ones, were used in the Baltimore museum (opened by Rembrandt in 1814), the New York museum (opened by Rubens in 1825), and probably also in the Utica museum (opened by Linnaeus in 1828). Now there are so many of this type of portrait so scattered that it is difficult to tell who painted which one when.

The fourth category of portraiture might be called the Peale family portrait. Since these portraits did not have to hold to the prescribed conventions demanded for the other categories, they range from the aston-

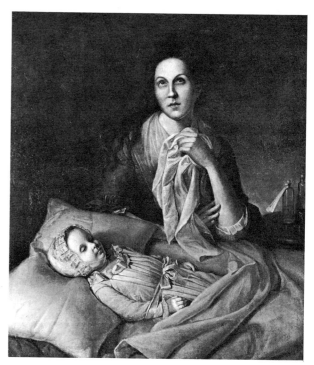

ishingly personal, such as *Rachel Weeping* (no. 9), to the unexpectedly inventive, such as *The Staircase Group* (no. 10) and *Exhuming the Mastodon* (no. 4). Of one of these Dr. Sellers wrote: "The conventions had to be sacrificed in order to perfect that other, essential artist's purpose, the illusion of reality. He painted his sons in the famous *Staircase Group* to show the young men [artist members] of the Columbianum what

4 EXHUMING THE MASTODON
by Charles Willson Peale

John Masten, owner of the site, climbs a ladder in the foreground, and Alexander Wilson, the ornithologist, stands to the left before a tent on the far bank. Members of the Peale family may be found to Wilson's left in order: Betsy and her little son Titian, James wearing a hat and gesturing in wonder, young Linnaeus and Franklin holding a floating cylinder in place. To the right, grouped about a drawing of bones, are C. W. Peale, Hannah, Rembrandt and wife, Rubens with Sybilla and Elizabeth, Raphaelle and wife. Coleman and Sophonisba Sellers hold an umbrella.

The Peale Museum

a painter of thirty years' experience could do, and the result was a triumph indeed, for General Washington took off his hat and bowed to it."

The *Mastodon* painting (no. 4) honors both the artist's family and his other love, natural history, the firm philosophic base of his Philadelphia Museum. "And although he still lacked confidence in his ability to paint 'history,' he was recording it at every stroke," Oliver Jensen astutely observed in his brilliant summary of the achievements of "The Peales" (*American Heritage* April 1955).

The other Peale professional portraitists naturally started in the style of their instructor Charles Willson Peale and gradually developed their own distinctive styles. That of James Peale is considered elsewhere in this catalog in articles by Dr. Sellers and E. Grosvenor Paine. Raphaelle Peale's own distinctive style in oils is poorly documented. A pair of portraits herein presented (no. 113-14) is attributed to him on the basis of their similarity to his miniatures.

Rembrandt Peale traveled a good deal in Europe and studied art in both London and Paris, where he learned the new "Classical Romanticism" of David and Gerard. His father was fascinated with his coloristic facility and applied the new technical "secrets" learned from his son in such works as *The Artist in his Museum* (no. 2) and *The Lamplight Portrait* (no. 7) more successfully than Rembrandt himself ever did. Rembrandt Peale became enmeshed in the

"historic" and "grandiose" tradition (no. 167) and his "Washington Cult" (no. 156-60), and finally, perhaps influenced by Thomas Sully, succumbed to Victorian sentimentality in such paintings as *The Pearl of Grief* (cf. no. 224).

The year of the Columbianum Exhibition (1795) at Philadelphia, sponsored by Charles Willson Peale, the first American academy of art, the first artists' exhibition held in America, saw the culmination of the genius of the first generation of the painting Peales.

10 THE STAIRCASE GROUP by C. W. Peale *Philadelphia Museum of Art*

7   THE LAMPLIGHT PORTRAIT
by C. W. Peale *The Detroit Institute of Arts*

As noted above, *The Staircase Group* (no. 10) was painted for this exhibition to set an example for the younger artists. It was the year of James Peale's *Family Group* (no. 72), a charming English conversation piece transplanted to America by an artist who had never set foot in England. It was the year of the "family" portrait by his brother showing the same artist in the prime of life as the successful *Miniature Painter* (no. 6), the year of some of his finest miniatures, family ones of his "new" sister-in-law (no. 78) and his alert and intelligent nephew (no. 77), and commissioned ones of Paul

Beck Jr. (no. 81) and Thomas Goodwin (no. 86). It was the year of the double portrait of the beautiful and talented Angelica with her doting but snobbish husband who "sat with a bad grace" to her father Charles

Willson Peale (no. 12). And it was the year that Washington sat to more Peales than ever before at one time, the last time he sat to any of them (the seventh time to Charles Willson, the only time to Rembrandt), the time Stuart punned he was "in danger of being *Pealed* all round" (no. 56, 156-57).

Another banner year in the productions of the Peales was 1822, the year of the great portraits by Charles Willson Peale, already noted above, acclaiming his museum (no. 2) and honoring his brother (no. 7), the retired miniature painter whose eyesight has failed him for this work, but who can enjoy a miniature of a pretty girl painted by his daughter Anna (no. 186). Failing eyesight or not, this was a banner time because it

156

was the time of James Peale's glorious still lifes, and of his nephew Raphaelle's discreet ones, too. The impetus for nephew and uncle to paint still lifes so abundantly at this time was probably given by the bountiful products—the "fruits of Belfield"—from Charles Willson Peale's country estate, then "near"

GEORGE WASHINGTON
by Rembrandt Peale (1795)
(above)
156   The Historical Society of Pennsylvania
(facing)
157 The Detroit Institute of Arts

Germantown (the mansion-house still stands, now in an urban environment).

If no other extraordinarily productive year such as these two—1795 and 1822—can be singled out, there certainly were significant periods. The years 1815-1820 were those of Charles Willson Peale's and James Peale's landscapes, also inspired by

199

66

Belfield (no. 65-67), of Rembrandt's frenzy over the *Court of Death* (no. 167) and of Titian's western sketches (no. 207-08). Titian Ramsay Peale (II), Charles Willson Peale's youngest son, was one of the first American artists to work beyond the Mississippi.

In the late 1820s Rembrandt Peale pioneered in America with the new art of lithography (no. 143, 148, 158) and taught the art to his eldest daughter Rosalba (no. 198-99) and his young son Michael Angelo (no. 219-20). For decades James Peale's daughters Maria, Anna, Margaretta and Sarah carried on the still-life tradition and

in the last decade of his life Rubens (1855-65) and his daughter Mary Jane revived it. Exposed to art all his life but prevented

158

Washington

From the Original Portrait Painted by Rembrandt Peale.

from practicing it earlier by poor eyesight, Rubens was an authentic "primitive." His nostalgic reinterpretation of the house in

which he was born, *The Old Museum* (no. 173), is as exciting as anything produced by that later French primitive of modern art, Henri Rousseau. And the small painting by

his uncle James, which inspired it (no. 100) is as basic and abstract as a Morandi.

This is the most comprehensive exhibition of works of art by members of the Peale Family ever held. It is not the largest. That distinction still goes to the pioneer show of modern times held at the Pennsylvania Academy of the Fine Arts in Philadelphia in 1923, "Exhibition of Portraits by Charles Willson Peale and James Peale and Rembrandt Peale" (317 portraits). As the name indicates, although it is still referred to in the literature, without date, as the "Peale Exhibition," it was restricted to three artists and to portraits. In the present exhibition there are twenty artists—albeit some may be represented by only one work—and both subjects and media are many.

The relationships of the artists in this exhibition to each other and the numerical order of their presentation (by date of birth) are as follows: Charles Willson Peale (1) and James Peale (2) were brothers. Charles Peale Polk (3) was the son of their sister Elizabeth. Raphaelle (4), Rembrandt (5), Rubens (6), Franklin (10) and Titian Ramsay Peale (13) were sons of Charles Willson Peale. Maria (7), Anna (9), Margaretta (11) and Sarah (15) were daughters of James Peale. Mary Jane Simes (16) was the daughter of James Peale's oldest daughter. James Peale's only son was James Peale Jr. (8), and Washington Peale (18) was the latter's son.

Rosalba (12) was the oldest of Rembrandt's eight daughters, Michael Angelo (17) was his younger son, and Harriet Cany (14) was Rembrandt's second wife. Mary

Jane (19) was Rubens Peale's only daughter. Coleman Sellers (20) was the son of Charles Willson Peale's daughter Sophonisba. With Coleman Sellers the art of photography is introduced, an art which even then was sounding the death knell of the art of the creative portrait painter, an art which provided sustenance for Peales of three generations in America.

Our aims for the exhibition—like the subjects and media represented—were also many. We wanted to show the best works by all the Peales, but in some cases we had to settle for the only work we could find. We wanted to give an adequate feeling for the "Gallery of Heroes" and so sometimes "personages" outweighed "art." We wanted to show—almost in person—various members of the Peale Family, some of whom painted themselves and each other enthusiastically and frequently. It is regretted that what would have been the eponymous picture of

33 JOHN PAUL JONES
by C. W. Peale
*Independence National
Historical Park*

the exhibition, *The Peale Family* of 1773, could not be made available. We wanted to show the range and versatility of the family, going as far afield as silhouettes—although who knows exactly who cut them—and medals. Yet, in spite of this, portraiture predominates, because here, and in still life, are to be found the best works of the family.

We did not ask for everything we would have liked, although some of our generous lenders may think we did. The favorable responses to our requests were overwhelming, and we thank all the lenders gratefully and appreciate the interest of those who were not able to contribute. All identifications of subjects and attributions to artists are those of the owners of the works shown. We are fully aware that some

of these—not many—are debatable. One of the purposes of an exhibition such as this is to bring together enough material to assist, perhaps, in solving such problems. In any case, all identifications and attributions were acceptable to the compiler of the catalog.

CHARLES H. ELAM

THE COURT OF DEATH by Rembrandt Peale. (above) 166   *Charles Coleman Sellers*, (below) 167   *The Detroit Institute of Arts*

97 *SIR PETER PARKER'S ATTACK AGAINST FORT MOULTRIE* by James Peale
Colonial Williamsburg

98 *THE GENERALS AT YORKTOWN* by James Peale. *Colonial Williamsburg*

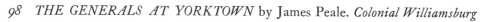

JAMES PEALE AND CHARLES WILLSON PEALE

by Charles Coleman Sellers

The successive Peale Family exhibitions, beginning with that at the Pennsylvania Academy of the Fine Arts in 1923, have each contributed something to the problems of distinguishing Peale from Peale. Gradually, in each museum or gallery, the individual styles have emerged more precisely, while the interwoven character of a family of painters, working closely together, was equally emphasized. There will always be intriguing points of doubt in these attributions, a generous share of them at the beginning of the story, with the two brothers, Charles and James.

James, as a boy, had been his brother's helper in the Annapolis saddlery, and after his brother's return from London in 1769 became frame-maker and student in the new business. We know that he could paint a creditable portrait by 1772, though very few of his early works have been identified. They would be virtually indistinguishable from his brother's. Resigning from the Conti-nental Army in 1779, his health more or less permanently shattered by three years of campaigning with the constantly embattled Maryland Line, he became again a studio assistant, helping with the full length *Washington* commissions and, later, producing his own versions of the piece. We have here a key piece in the establishment of his own pro-fessional identity, his *Generals at Yorktown* (no. 98). It is a history painting, though intended also for use in the *Washingtons*, to bring the battle background up to date. It might be evidence, incidentally, that James had marched with his old regiment from Philadelphia to Virginia, and shared as a volunteer in the siege operations. James' view of the action at Fort Moultrie (no. 97) shows again that he had been inspired, like young John Trumbull, to record the great events of the Revolution in historical art. As a portraitist, he seems to have been favored by fellow officers of the old regular army.

Yet James continues obscure, often in need of his brother's aid and always receiving it. In 1786 Charles retired from miniature painting with the idea that specialization would help them both. "James is well," he wrote, "and I hope going into a hurry of business. I have left off painting in miniature, lowered my price in the large portraits in order to fill up that space of time which would have been spent in the other branch, and James paints miniatures at 3 guineas each. Now if we do not get business times will be very hard for us." And in 1787 to Joseph Howell, whose portrait in uniform is probably by James, "James desires his best respects to you. Poor fellow! At last he is getting into some tolerable business which I hope will continue."

The Peale brothers have emerged together also as poets of a sort, and a newspaper effusion of 1788, signed "I. P.," is surely from the pen of the younger one. It pours out praises from a grateful and admiring heart, extolling in particular Charles' painting of General Reed in the action at Whitemarsh, a fragment of which survives in the collections of the Historical Society of Pennsylvania. It reveals that the poet himself has been painted by this same hand—

> On me of humbler fame, thy paints bestow,
> Eternal bloom, and cheeks that always glow.

It is at this time, however, that James is coming into his own with a style distinct from his brother's and interesting in its own right. His long and successful career as a miniaturist is defined not only by the "I. P."

signature with date, but by the stylized mouth and often rather rigidly upright pose. His pieces lack the air of intimacy and tenderness found in many of his brother's, painted earlier when the miniature was more wholly a private art. By the late 1780s the ivory was larger and the pictures worn openly rather than in a locket, a fashion which certainly makes the more impersonal presentation appropriate. The general formula of James' later miniatures, as one can see it here, surely owes something also to the military blazonry of the Napoleonic period, as adapted to popular fashion.

It should be noted that the brothers' agreement to specialize was not strictly observed. James, touring in Maryland or elsewhere, would paint a canvas if asked to, and similarly, Charles a miniature. But there is a different aspect now in their portraits. Those of the elder brother are still in the spirit of the eighteenth century enlightenment, relaxed, characterized by an air of rational affability. Those of James, in contrast, feel the new romantic mood coming in with the turn of the century. There is often a wistful sadness in these faces, and the landscape background, which with Charles would have been probably a portrait of the subject's home acres, is here simply, as in his lovely *Jane Ramsay Peale* (no. 73), an artistic reinforcement of the mood of the whole. As one reviews the work of a portraitist, one can often glimpse that tendency to infuse into the sitter some essence of himself. In James Peale's faces we can see,

73

perhaps, not only the mood of the times but something also of the temperament of this painter, beset by ill-health and poverty, working with patient dedication through a long life brightened by interests, excursions, a gay young family.

In contrast to his exuberant brother, James Peale left almost no documentation of his life. The American Philosophical Society has one sketch book, an important record (no. 99), and a recently discovered design for a transparency honoring the return of Lafayette in 1824, reminding us

that James also filled the windows of his house with transparent paintings as news of the victories of the Revolution came in. But one must see him almost wholly through others' eyes, and at that only occasionally. In 1789 he assisted Francis Hopkinson in an experimental project for drawing landscape. We see him, when patronage was hard to find, doing jobs for the flourishing Peale's Museum, or at a table near the physiogno-trace making over Museum silhouettes into water color profiles. Later, in the 1820s, there was something of a renaissance for James. His fruit pieces have a quality of opulence that made them more popular than Raphaelle's stark and rather crystaline pieces. He and his brother took up land-scape painting together, and in a style to be echoed in greater richness by James Peale Jr. Anna, Margaretta and Sarah came into the scene as studio assistants, and one finds some of the gouty old soldier's solidly composed portraits brightened by fabrics and embroideries such as are to be found in the later work of Sarah Miriam Peale.

99

It is for this exhibition, and for the scholarship which it will stimulate, to even the balance a little more by bringing James farther and more openly into view. Scholars will find what an anonymous newspaper writer of a century ago described—"An accomplished and highly esteemed gentleman, as well as an admirable painter; yet quiet and unassuming in both characters, shrinking from public laudation and puffing, while his devotion to the labor he loved, and its results, richly deserves all praise."

72 THE ARTIST AND HIS FAMILY
James Peale with his wife, Mary Chambers Claypoole, and children, from left to right,
Jane Ramsay, James Jr., Maria, Margaretta Angelica, and Anna Claypoole
The Pennsylvania Academy of the Fine Arts

MINIATURISTS IN THE PEALE FAMILY

by E. Grosvenor Paine

There are certain traits to be found in all the Peale artists who painted in miniature, probably the most intimate form of art, from Charles Willson Peale (1741-1827) through Mary Jane Simes (1807-1872), his grand-niece. A wiry technique, evident in Charles Willson's later miniatures, comes forth strongly in the miniatures by his brother James (1749-1831) painted in 1790 and after, and is especially evident in the miniatures of Anna Claypoole Peale (1791-1878) and Mary Jane Simes, less often in those of Raphaelle Peale (1774-1825). The miniatures of Charles Willson and James often show a greenish-gray tone not as prevalent in the others.

The Peales, with the exception of Charles Willson, had another trait in common: they were not afraid to sign their works, boldly and in plain view. James painted his signature "I.P." ("J.P.") on most of his miniatures. Raphaelle followed his uncle and sometimes went so far as to sign his surname

with the subject's age, as in the miniature of *Benjamin F. Pearce* (no. 120). Anna and her cousin both scratched their names in full, generally with the date. In later years when Anna became Mrs. Staughton, and then Mrs. Duncan, she signed on the reverse of the miniature.

Charles Willson Peale found miniatures to his liking early in his career. He studied under Benjamin West in London, coming with requests from families in the colonies to have their English relatives "set " to him. His miniatures, typical of miniatures of the 1760s in England, are small. Charles Willson's miniatures have a great deal in common with another of his teachers, John Singleton Copley, in coloring, technique and size. Both artists were probably influenced by the English miniaturists, Nathaniel Hone and Charles Dixon (during his stay in London in 1757 Benjamin Franklin "set" to Charles Dixon), and characteristics of the works of both of these artists appear in

Peale's work. Charles Willson's miniatures are low in tone value and, even when a red is used, the bluish-green tones come through. He formed his shadows with short stubby strokes about the face and on the costume. Details in headdresses, laces or ornaments, especially in women's clothing, as in most of the Peale family's works, are carefully drawn. He painted the eyes of his men wide open, while the eyes of most of his women seem to droop a little, giving a demure shyness that emphasizes intimacy, the purpose of the miniatures. The upper eyelids are outlined in almost a solid line. His early

miniatures all possess a rare softness found in no other Peale except Raphaelle. The few miniatures he painted after 1789 seem to take on the feeling and wiry technique of James. An example of this is the 1798 miniature of *Mrs. Gerard DePeyster* (no. 26). His subjects' faces glow against his dark backgrounds, giving the entire ivory a gem-like quality. Most of these miniatures have dark backgrounds—blackish-green going into the lighter green on the subject's left. All of Charles Willson's miniatures have a straight-forward appeal that places them high on the list of great miniatures.

James Peale worked much in the manner of his elder brother until well into the 1790s. It has been said that Charles Willson at times could not tell his own miniatures from those of his brother. Examples of this simi-

26

19

larity are *William Bingham*, a Charles Willson Peale (no. 19), and *Paul Beck Jr.*, a James Peale (no. 81), both found in the

almost a pursed smile. Judging from the number of known miniatures painted by him, he was the most prolific of the family.

81   PAUL BECK JR. by James Peale
Museum of Art, Carnegie Institute

95

DuPuy Collection. After 1795 James developed his own style and his colors are not faded like those of his brother, but seem to come forth stronger, with a different long hairy stroke that is shadowed into the face. He painted the clothing in a looser manner, shading folds with longer hatching, and the treatment of the hair flows in long wiry strokes, especially in the case of *Mrs. John Wilson* (no. 95). James' backgrounds broke away from one color, shaded in various tones, into the sky and clouds, achieved by interlaced long hatchings instead of the singular hatching of his early miniatures. The one characteristic James kept through his entire career is the curve of the lips into

Raphaelle painted in a freer style. Most of his male portraits are in a pattern, three-quarters dexter, with gaze directed to the spectator. He gave his sitters high cheek bones, almost a swollen effect, lips turned up at the corners, upper eyelids heavily outlined, creating a deep-set sunken look. The shading of the face is achieved by long hairy strokes. On most of his men there is a slight double chin. The style of the coat worn suggests sloped shoulders and, when buttoned to the top, even the slightest man has a pinched "little brother's coat" look. The hair comes through with the typical Peale wiry manner. Most of his backgrounds are free of hatching except around the upper part of the subject's head and on both sides of the shoulders. A fine example of all of these characteristics is illustrated in the miniature of an unknown young man from

the DuPuy Collection (no. 123). The two exceptions are *Robert Oliphant* (no. 119) and the vigorous portrait of a man in a gray coat (no. 118), both miniatures having heavy dark cross-hatched backgrounds.

Rembrandt Peale (1778-1860), the younger brother of Raphaelle, is credited with painting miniatures in the early years of the nineteenth century. Some miniatures signed "R.P." were given to him by students of the Peale cult, but have been found to be definitely the works of Raphaelle. There are miniatures in both private and public collections said to be by Rembrandt, one being

of *Washington Irving* in the R. W. Norton Collection (no. 146). It has been much overpainted so what one might discover of the technique of Rembrandt has almost disappeared. With no other proof of signed ones, students of American miniatures must be satisfied with attributions.

Anna Claypoole Peale started painting in the tight detailed style of her father James. In fact a few of the miniatures signed by James around 1815 could well be taken for the work of Anna; for example, the portrait of a man at Utica, signed and dated 1813 (no. 96), in technique is similar to her *Self-Portrait* at Chicago, signed and dated 1818 (no. 181). Both have a close resemblance in style, handling and color—the skin tones lifted by hairy strokes, fine short strokes forming a solid line for the upper eyelids,

96   *181*

190   *ANDREW JACKSON* by Anna C. Peale
Yale University Art Gallery

slight dark marks at the corners of the mouth giving the same pursed smile, wiry short and long strokes giving the hair an almost wispy quality. The background is handled in a latticed manner. Later in life Anna used a slightly looser style following the trend of miniature painting, but she continued to use her same backgrounds. There have been a few examples of sky and cloud backgrounds, deftly handled, as in the fine miniature of *Andrew Jackson*, signed and dated 1819 (no. 190). She generally painted on ovals of ivory, but her miniatures of Rosalba (no. 186) and of Rosalba's father, her cousin Rembrandt (no. 185), foreshadow the larger cabinet size miniature which replaced the more intimate miniature that was worn.

Sarah Miriam Peale (1800-1885) is listed as having painted miniatures, but like Rembrandt she did not sign any; therefore few attributions may be accepted until proof has been established.

Mary Jane Simes painted in very much the same manner as Anna, although her work was a little more primitive, especially in the handling of the subject, which was often placed low on the ivory. Her colors are harsh and hard, at times coming direct from her palette without toning up or down. Judging from the known examples, she seems to have practiced professionally only from 1825 to 1835 (no. 218).

The Peales always strived to do the inter-

218

186

185

esting and unusual in producing their works of art. Four members of the family are represented by one of the paintings in this exhibition, an oil portrait by Charles Willson Peale of James Peale studying a miniature of Rosalba painted by Anna (no. 7). This identical miniature (no. 186), together with quite a few others by some of the artists considered in this article, is in the exhibition. Although only a fraction of their total production, these works are a testament of the contribution of the family to the intimate art of the miniature.

The Peale Family (dated 1773), canvas 56½ x 89½ by C. W. Peale. *The New-York Historical Society* (not in the exhibition). From left to right: St. George, C. W. Peale, James, Margaret Ramsay, Rachel (probably with same daughter as in no. 9), Peggy Durgan (nurse), Eleanor (died in infancy), Elizabeth Polk, and the artist's mother. Argus, the dog, was added later when the painting was reworked (c. 1808).

STILL LIFE PAINTINGS
BY THE PEALE FAMILY

by Edward H. Dwight

Charles Willson Peale, who considered still life painting practice for beginners and pastime for amateurs, exhibited only one still life during his long life—*Apples, &c.* —probably done in 1815 at Belfield, his farm near Philadelphia. In 1817 the elderly Peale asked his oldest son Raphaelle to come to Belfield and sit for his likeness. The portrait he painted shows Raphaelle seated on a chair before an easel, holding a palette

6 *JAMES PEALE*
PAINTING A MINIATURE
by C. W. Peale
Amherst College

11 RAPHAELLE PEALE
by C. W. Peale
Mr. and Mrs. William L. Page

and brushes in his swollen, arthritic hands. Hanging behind him is a painting of apples, probably his father's 1815 still life which, in subject matter and informal arrangement, resembles the fruit, knife and plate found in C. W. Peale's early family group at the New-York Historical Society.

Smiling pleasantly in this large conversation piece is James Peale, who exhibited one painting of fruit in the exhibition of the Columbianum held at Philadelphia in 1795. It was not until 1823, however, that James exhibited another fruit piece, but from the following year until his death in 1831 he frequently exhibited still lifes at the Pennsylvania Academy of the Fine Arts. Several fruit pieces of the early 1820s by James, which have a classical purity, are very similar. On a bare wooden table, he arranged a Chinese export porcelain dish filled with fruit topped with grapes and grape leaves, while on the table he carefully arranged other pieces of fruit, with some grapes dangling over the fore edge of the table. Seated in a chair, James painted them in the tight, controlled manner of his large portraits. The background is plain, light on one side, dark on the other, while the light falls from left to right. All of these were painted on wood panels and one, which includes a rotten apple on the table, was copied six times by Rubens Peale and probably by other members of the Peale clan as well. In the copies that have been located, a few of which are signed and none of which is on wood, the rotten apple has

been changed to unspoilt fruit. Unless a painting is signed, it is difficult to determine which Peale is its author. Some of the Peales made replicas of their own works and copies of still lifes by relatives.

All of the Peales painted still lifes early in their careers while some, like James, took it up again in old age; but only James and his nephew Raphaelle mastered the art. They were undoubtedly influenced by 17th century European still life paintings they saw exhibited in Philadelphia by such artists as Caravaggio, Kalf, van Os, Snyders, and Ruysch. At the Columbianum exhibition of 1795, in which James exhibited one fruit piece, Raphaelle exhibited eight, and by the time James took up still life in earnest, Raphaelle had produced some of his finest works. In his best still lifes, Raphaelle expresses the quiet delight generated in him by the few modest objects he put on the table before him—a great variety of fruits, vegetables, meat, flowers, bakery goods, containers, and other objects such as books, eggs, cheese, oysters, and even a miniature of a lady! There is variety, too, in the sizes of panel or canvas on which he painted, and almost every inscription is unique. Raphaelle's love of joking found its way into these inscriptions: on one painting he wrote "Raphäel Peale," another is dated "A.D 1818." There is a wide range in the arrangement of the objects on a bare table top; sometimes they fill the space, at other times a few objects are completely surrounded by the flat table and wall. Two of the most

134

124

original paintings in American art are the still life owned by Wadsworth Atheneum, with its daring arrangement and handsome colors (no. 132), and his famous *After the Bath* at Kansas City (no. 124), which Raphaelle painted as a practical joke on his nagging wife. Raphaelle had a penchant for deceptions and a fondness for liquor—five of his still lifes contain wine—but unfortunately he was not content with only painting it. Some of Raphaelle's last still lifes, painted in 1822, large fruit pieces that contain slices of watermelons, were not done in his own unselfconscious, relaxed style, but in the pristine manner of his uncle James' work of the same year (no. 133).

Most of the still lifes James painted during the last decade of his life contain grapes, watermelon, peaches, and apples, many painted in a soft, unsteady manner. But four of his last and finest still lifes are vegetable pieces. One of them, a strong, daring painting, is reminiscent of Raphaelle's

earlier informal arrangement and rough technique.

133

Most of James Peale's children painted one or more still lifes. Maria's first attempt was a vegetable piece exhibited in the Pennsylvania Academy in 1811, the only painting she exhibited there. James Peale Jr.'s copy of Raphaelle's *Peaches and Grapes* was exhibited at the Academy in 1829, a rare still life by him. Anna Claypoole Peale exhibited her first attempt, a fruit piece, in 1811, and *Grapes* in 1817. Her major output was miniatures. James' two youngest daughters, however, devoted more of their energy to still life.

Evidently both Rembrandt and Titian R. Peale shared their father's low opinion of still life painting. Titian exhibited one still life in 1822 at Baltimore, and Rembrandt exhibited a painting of fruit in 1825 and a still life in 1838 and 1839. In 1801 he painted one of his finest works, a portrait of his brother Rubens with a geranium plant (no. 139). The large plant in bloom, the first brought to America, is painted with great

skill. Rubens, who was seventeen when this portrait was painted, had already begun his long career as a museum man. He was 71 when he took up painting on his farm near Schuylkill Haven. He kept a record of the paintings he did during the last decade of his life, and most of these were still lifes— flowers, fruit, vegetables, cake and wine— done with charm and sincerity. Often they were copies after James or Raphaelle; sometimes he was assisted in his paintings by his children, particularly Mary Jane, who also painted many still lifes on her own. The 131st painting on Rubens' list is a copy of a still life with white watermelon by his uncle James. It was his last painting. Taken ill at the easel, he died that same day, July 17, 1865. Rubens Peale's long life spanned the active years of still life painting by members of the Peale family. No other family in early America has contributed as much to this humble, colorful, and delightful form of art.

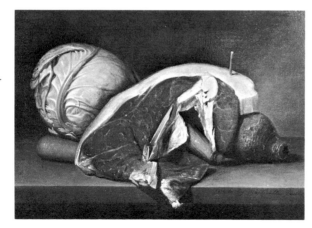

131

171

CATALOG

NOTE: Page numbers in margins give pages on which some works are illustrated. References and bibliography are in the back of the book.

3

1

CHARLES WILLSON PEALE

*(1741 Queen Annes County, Md.—
Philadelphia 1827)*

was a saddler's apprentice in Annapolis before his majority. Then he studied painting very briefly with John Hesselius in Maryland (1763) and John

Singleton Copley in Boston (1765), before extended training with Benjamin West in London (1767-69). His early works as an itinerant portrait painter in Maryland, Pennsylvania, and Virginia show the successive influence of these artists.

There is a fine portrait of the young Charles Willson Peale by Benjamin West at the New-York Historical Society. Peale was not West's first

American pupil in London, for Matthew Pratt and Abraham Delanoy Jr. preceded him; Copley, Earl, Trumbull, Wright, Brown, Stuart, Sully, Rembrandt Peale, Allston, Morse, and others, followed.

C. W. Peale painted seven life portraits of George Washington, his (and the subject's) first at Mount Vernon (1772), and last at Philadelphia (1795). Peale believed anybody could be trained to be an artist and tried to teach his brothers and sisters, sons and daughters, nephews and nieces, etc. Several of them assisted in completing the details of his various Washingtons and their replicas, for which there was a great demand for a time.

Just before the Revolution he settled in Philadelphia and served with the Continental Army until 1778, attaining the rank of captain and not neglecting the opportunity to make small portraits and miniatures of his deserving military associates. His display of some of these in the painting room of his house in Philadelphia attracted such interest that it developed into a museum devoted also to natural history and science, in his own words "a world in miniature"—the first scientific museum in America. The museum was moved for larger quarters first to Philosophical Hall (1794) and then to the old State House or Independence Hall (1802-27). In his later years the admission fees gave him a good income.

In 1762 C. W. Peale married Rachel Brewer and named many of their children for artists; some children of his next wife Elizabeth DePeyster, whom he married in 1791, were named for scientists; Hannah Moore, his third wife (married 1805), had no children. He painted little on commission after the turn of the century, devoting himself to running the museum or to scientific pursuits, and tried to steer painting commissions to his brother James or his own sons, especially Rembrandt, whose French training influenced his art, for son now taught the father in his sixties.

FAMILY PORTRAITS

1   SELF-PORTRAIT IN UNIFORM

Capt. Peale (1741-1827)

Canvas 6 x 5½ / 1777/78 / Once attributed to James Peale
Coll.: Charles Coleman Sellers (desc.)
Exh.: New London 1944 no. 89 / Peale 1954 no. 29 / —1963 no. 1
Ref.: Sellers no. 625, 376 / —1939 / Briggs 1952 / Jensen 1955 / APS 1961
American Philosophical Society Library, Philadelphia

2   THE ARTIST IN HIS MUSEUM

In 1827 the museum was moved to the Arcade; 1838 the Chinese Museum; 1844 Masonic Hall; 1854 dispersed.

Canvas 103½ x 80 / 1822 / For a study of the "Long Room" in Independence Hall, used for the background, started by CWP and finished by his son Titian, see no. 209.
Coll.: PPM (*sale* 1854 no. 258) / L. H. Newbold / Joseph Harrison
Exh.: PAFA 1822 no. 300 / Cincinnati 1852 no. 258 / Peale 1923 no. 144 / —1953 no. 25 / —1954 no. 28 / MMA 1939 no. 61 / Phila. 1940 no. 52 / —1944 no. 18 / —1955 no. 3 / Pittsburgh 1940 no. 77 / Brooklyn 1957 no. 20
Ref.: Sellers no. 636, 383 / —1947 / Tuckerman 1867 / PAFA 1902 / Caffin 1907 / Dunlap 1918 / Isham 1927 / Jackman 1928 / Cahill 1935 / Flexner 1939 / Shoolman 1942 / Barker 1950 / Robb 1951 / Briggs 1952 / Roos 1954 / Jensen 1955 / *Life* 28 Mar. 1955 / Richardson 1956 / Mendelowitz 1960 / Pierson 1960 / UP 1965 MH30
The Pennsylvania Academy of the Fine Arts (*gift of Mrs. Joseph Harrison 1878*), *Philadelphia*

3   SELF-PORTRAIT WITH A MASTODON BONE

"In the Character of a Naturalist"

Canvas 26 x 22 / 1824 / Last self-portrait, done "for the multitude" / Companion to self-portrait "in

the Character of a Painter" at PAFA (Sellers no. 638)

Coll.: Sybilla Peale Summers (dau.) and desc.

Exh.: PAFA 1824 no. 68 / Peale 1923 no. 176 / — 1953 no. 4 / BPM 1956 no. 56

Ref.: Sellers no. 639, 384 / NYHS 1941 no. 579 / *Art Qu.* Aut. 1945 / *Bull.* Jan. 1962

The New-York Historical Society, New York

4 EXHUMING THE MASTODON

"The Mammoth Picture" / Romantic record of the first American scientific expedition excavation / The remains of two more or less complete skeletons were recovered from this and other finds and were mounted. One, shown at APS and PPM (giving it international recognition), was later acquired by P. T. Barnum and destroyed by fire. The other was taken by Rembrandt and/or Rubens on tour in England and America (1802-04), later was featured at PBM (1814-30), and now (dismantled) belongs to AMNH. (See no. 3, 163, 204, and pamphlets by Rembrandt.)

In painting the crowd constantly present at the site in Ulster County, N. Y., CWP amused himself by filling in with likenesses of family and friends. Of those actually there in August 1801, only the artist, his son Rembrandt, and John Masten, owner of the land, are identifiable. Although dated 1806, CWP kept adding figures until 1808. On 16 Dec. 1807 he wrote Benjamin West that it contained upwards of 50 figures, including 18 portraits. (Letter is quoted in full in Sellers *CWP and 'The Mammoth Picture'* BPM 1951.) The finished work has about 75 figures and at least 20 portraits. Masten climbs a ladder in the foreground. Alexander Wilson, arms folded, stands by tent at left, his presence celebrating recent publication of his *Ornithology* (cf. portrait by Rembrandt at APS). In the group to right of Wilson are Maj. John Stagg, Mrs. Stagg, then her sister Betsy DePeyster Peale (d. 1804), warning her little son Titian II of the approaching storm. James Peale

stands in the narrow opening between two poles, hat on head, in a theatrical gesture of wonder toward the dig. Just right of the wheel, young Linnaeus and Franklin (sons) hold a floating cylinder in place. In the group at the right, behind a large drawing of bones, stand left to right CWP with arm extended, Hannah M. Peale (m. 1805) in her Quaker cap, Mrs. Rembrandt Peale (?), Rembrandt, Rubens (sons) with his spectacles and with little Sybilla and Elizabeth (their half-sisters) in front of him, Mrs. Raphaelle Peale (?), and Raphaelle. Coleman and Sophonisba Sellers (daughter), sheltered by a green umbrella, are in back of this group. (Adapted from description with Sellers no. 252)

Canvas 50 x 62½ / Signed and dated lower right *p. 15* *C W Peale*/1806

Coll.: PPM (*sale* 1854) / Lloyd Rogers / George Reuling (*sale* New York 26 Apr. 1905 no. 30) / Bertha James White

Exh.: APS 1808-10 / MMA 1939 no. 60 / Phila. 1940 no. 51 / Pittsburgh 1940 no. 78 / Buffalo 1948 (?) / Washington 1950 no. 89 / Denver 1952 / Peale 1954 no. 1 / —1965 no. 44 / Whitney 1954 no. 27 / —1966 no. 210 / BPM 1956 no. 55

Ref.: Sellers no. 252, 285 / —1947 / —*op. cit.* / *Life* 19 June 1939 / Larkin 1949 / Barker 1950 / Flexner 1950 / —1954 / *NGM* Feb. 1951 / Briggs 1952 / *Art in Am.* Oct. 1954 / Jensen 1955 / Richardson 1956 / Eliot 1957 / Pierson 1960 / BPM 1964 / UP 1965 MH29

The Trustees of the Municipal Museum of Baltimore Inc., The Peale Museum (gift of Mrs. Harry White in memory of her husband 1948)

5 JAMES PEALE

The artist's youngest brother (1749-1831)

Miniature 1⁹⁄₁₆ x 1¼ / 1788 (?)

Exh.: MMA 1963 no. 238

Ref.: Sellers no. 657 (?)

J. William Middendorf II

5

8

6 *JAMES PEALE PAINTING A MINIATURE*

p. 35   Canvas 30 x 25 / 1795 / Companion piece of the artist's sister-in-law is also at Amherst (Sellers no. 661)

Coll.: Mabel Peale Elder (desc. of both subject and artist)

Exh.: Peale 1923 no. 68 / —1954 no. 30 / Washington 1925 no. 42 / Chicago 1949 no. 87 / Colorado Springs 1949 no. 31 / Amherst 1950 / Washington 1960 no. 22 / Milwaukee 1966 no. 74

Ref.: Sellers no. 658, 266 / —1939 / *International Studio* Feb. 1920 / *Antiques* Oct. 1932 / Pratt 1946 / *Art in Am.* Dec. 1950

Amherst College (bequest of Herbert Lee Pratt 1945), Amherst, Mass.

7 *JAMES PEALE ("THE LAMPLIGHT PORTRAIT")*

p. 17   Canvas 24½ x 36 / 1822 / Done following the above (no. 2) likewise to honor his brother, who examines a miniature by his daughter Anna of the artist's granddaughter (no. 186)

Coll.: PPM (*sale* 1854 no. 88) / Augustin Runyon Peale

Exh.: Cincinnati 1852 no. 88 / Peale 1923 no. 192 / —1954 no. 31 / Penn. 1955 no. 8 / Detroit 1957 no. 42 / Hartford 1964 no. 214 / Whitney 1966 no. 211

Ref.: Sellers no. 659, 336 / —1947 / *Bull.* 1950-51: 1 / *Art Qu.* Aut. 1950 / Flexner 1954 / Jensen 1955 / *Arts* Sep. 1956 / Richardson 1956 / Pierson 1960 / Detroit 1966

The Detroit Institute of Arts (gift of Dexter M. Ferry Jr. 1950)

8 *MRS. CHARLES WILLSON PEALE*
Rachel Brewer (1744-90), the artist's first wife

Miniature 2⅞ x 2⅛ / c. 1769 / Probably used for similar portrait in a miniature with her daughter Eleanor, b. 1770 (Sellers no. 642 / Wehle 1927)

Coll.: Rubens Peale and desc.

Exh.: MMA 1963 no. 236

Ref.: Sellers no. 641 / Wharton 1898 / Bolton 1921 no. 15

J. William Middendorf II

9 RACHEL WEEPING

Rachel mourning death of her daughter Margaret (b. and d. 1772)

p. 14 Canvas 37⅛ x 32¼ / 1772-1818
Coll.: Sellers (desc.)
Exh.: New London 1944 no. 89 / NYHS 1948 no. 16 / Detroit 1957 no. 39 / Peale 1963 no. 9
Ref.: Sellers no. 645, 49 / —1939 / Flexner 1954 / Jensen 1955
Charles Coleman Sellers

10 THE STAIRCASE GROUP

Raphaelle and Titian Ramsay Peale, the artist's sons / "A Deception" with Titian I above left / Titian Ramsay (1780-98), named for the great Venetian artist and for his aunt Margaret's husband, Col. Nathaniel Ramsay (not the Scottish portrait painter Allan Ramsay), was himself the namesake for his step-mother's next child, born after his death. / APS has a MS manual on miniature painting written by Titian I (Peale 1963 no. 103).

Canvas 89 x 39½ / 1795 / Once signed lower right on card
Coll.: PPM (*sale* 1854 no. 100) / L. H. Newbold / Mrs. Sabin Colton Jr., Bryn Mawr / Dr. Harold S. Colton (desc.)
Exh.: Phila. 1795 no. 61 / —1940 no. 53 / —1955 no. 8 / Cincinnati 1852 no. 100 / Peale 1923 no. 255/—1944 no. 4/—1953 no. 32/San Francisco 1935 no. 15 / Baltimore 1938 no. 4 / MMA 1939 no. 55 / Pittsburgh 1940 no. 75 / London 1946 no. 162 / Chicago 1949 no. 88 / Wildenstein 1953 no. 8 / —1957 / Minneapolis 1963 no. 23 / St. Louis 1964 no. 7 / St. Petersburg 1965 no. 2
Ref.: Sellers no. 662, 268 / —1947 / *Crayon* Apr. 1856 / Burroughs 1936 / *Art Qu.* Aut. 1939 / *Mag. of Art* June 1939 / *Bull.* May 1940 / —(Ann. Rep.) 1946 / St. Gaudens 1941 / Walker and James 1943 / Larkin 1949 / Barker 1950 / Walker 1951 / Briggs 1952 / Flexner 1954 / Roos 1954 / Taylor 1954 / Jensen 1955 / Richardson 1956 / Eliot

1957 / Pierson 1960 / Upjohn 1963 / Huyghe 1964 / Stoudt 1964 / UP 1965 MH28

Commissioners of Fairmount Park (George W. Elkins Collection 1945), courtesy of the Philadelphia Museum of Art

11 RAPHAELLE PEALE

The artist's eldest son (1774-1825)

p. 35 Canvas 26 x 22 / 1817/18
Coll.: Martha G. Peale / Mrs. Robert Lane (Marion Penrose Peale)
Exh.: PAFA 1819 no. 169
Ref.: Sellers no. 663 / *Life* 30 Mar. 1942 / Bury in *Am. Coll.* Aug. 1948 / Jensen 1955
Mr. and Mrs. William L. Page

12 ANGELICA AND ALEXANDER ROBINSON

Angelica Kauffman Peale (1775-1853), the artist's eldest daughter to survive infancy, married 1794 Alexander Robinson (1751-1845), successful Baltimore businessman from Ireland. Angelica was named for a dashing Swiss lady artist whom her father met in England (they were exact contemporaries). / Angelica painted in her youth, and grasps her father's brush in his portrait with her now at Bayou Bend, Houston, Tex. (Sellers no. 626).

p. 18 Canvas 26¼ x 35¼ / 1795 / In his diary CWP said his son-in-law "sat with a bad grace." / A replica, started in 1795 but finished later, belongs to the family, St. Louis, Mo. (Sellers no. 743)
Coll.: George Rowan Robinson, St. Louis / Anne Randolph Robinson Edgar, Minneapolis / Marjorie Edgar, Marine-on-St. Croix, Minn. (desc.)
Ref.: Sellers no. 742 / —1947 / Peale 1965 no. 7
Miss Page Robinson

13 (CHARLES) LINNAEUS PEALE

The artist's second wife's eldest surviving son (1794-1832). Sometime soldier, sailor, politician, and assistant at the family museums, he was named for

a Swedish scientist (1707-78), the founder of modern systematic botany. In 1828 he opened his own museum in Utica, N. Y., on Genesee St., and probably then featured the large *Court of Death* by his brother Rembrandt (no. 167). Lin was a native of Philadelphia, where he died.

Canvas 26 x 22 / 1818
Coll.: Augustin R. Peale / Algernon T. Peale / Francis D. Peale, Utica, N. Y. (desc.)
Ref.: Sellers no. 620, 314 / —1947 / Jensen 1955
Dr. and Mrs. Lysle N. Harrington

14 MRS. CHARLES WILLSON PEALE

Hannah Moore (1755-1821), third wife of the artist (m. 1805); he did her miniature at the time of their marriage and her portrait with his daughter Elizabeth soon thereafter (Sellers no. 651-52).

Canvas 24⅛ x 20⅛ / Signed and dated lower right *C. W Peale/painted* 1816
Coll.: Deborah Moore Jackson (sister), Phila. / Harriet Jackson Iddings / Mary Iddings Parker / Rev. Henry Ainsworth Parker / Reginald Seabury Parker, Cambridge, Mass.
Ref.: Sellers no. 653, 308
Museum of Fine Arts, Boston

14

15

OTHER PORTRAITS AND MINIATURES

15 JOHN QUINCY ADAMS (1767-1848)

Sixth President of the United States (1825-29), whose father was also portrayed by CWP (1791/94, INHP; Sellers no. 3)

Canvas 24 x 20 / 1818
Coll.: PPM (*sale* 1854 no. 142)
Exh.: Cincinnati 1852 no. 142 / Peale 1923 no. 36 /— 1953 no. 14 / —1954 no. 3 / New York 1941 / Madison 1952
Ref.: Sellers 1952 no. 4, 331 / HSP 1942
The Historical Society of Pennsylvania (gift of Charles S. Ogden 1896), Philadelphia

16 FRANCIS BAILEY (c. 1735-1815)

Official printer for Congress and the State of Pennsylvania, and Philadelphia newspaper publisher.

Canvas 26 x 21¾ / 1791
Coll.: Abigail Bailey James (dau.) / John Henry James / Margaret Lynch James, Urbana, Ohio
Exh.: Peale 1954 no. 5
Ref.: Sellers no. 14 / —in *Antiques* Dec. 1954 / *Bull. Hist. and Phil. Soc. Ohio* July 1950 / *Bull.* Oct. 1958
Cincinnati Art Museum

17 MRS. FRANCIS BAILEY
Eleanor Miller

Canvas 26 x 21¾ / 1791
Coll. and Ref.: See companion piece, above.
Exh.: Peale 1954 no. 6
Cincinnati Art Museum

17

16

18 *JOSHUA BARNEY (1759-1818)*
Naval Officer

Canvas 23 x 20 / 1784/85 / An unrelated post-
humous portrait of Barney was commissioned from
Rembrandt Peale, 1818 by the City of Baltimore
(BPM 1956 no. 67)
Coll.: PPM (*sale* 1854 no. 41) / City of Philadelphia
(on permanent loan to INHP 1951)
Exh.: Cincinnati 1852 no. 41
Ref.: Sellers no. 21, 157 / Wood 1927 / Jensen 1955
Independence National Historical Park, Philadelphia

19 *WILLIAM BINGHAM (1751-1804)*
Philadelphia financier

p. 30   *Miniature* 1⅝ x 1¼ / c. 1780
Coll.: Titian R. Peale 1908
Exh.: Peale 1923 no. 302 / 1954 no. 44 / MMA

1927 / Washington 1932 no. 103
Ref.: Sellers no. 48, 422 / Bolton 1921 no. 1
Museum of Art, Carnegie Institute (The Herbert DuPuy Collection 1927), Pittsburgh

20 CAPT. JOSEPH BRANT (1742-1807)
Thayendanegea, Chief of the Mohawks / He was also portrayed by Benjamin West c. 1775 (with Col. Guy Johnson, NGA)

Canvas 25½ x 21¼ / 1797
Coll.: PPM (*sale* 1854 no. 129) / City of Philadelphia (on permanent loan to INHP 1951)
Exh.: Cincinnati 1852 no. 129
Ref.: Sellers no. 79, 253 / Gabriel 1929 / Lee 1929 / *Antiques* May 1958
Independence National Historical Park, Philadelphia

21 WILLIAM BUCKLAND (1734-74)
Southern architect, shown with plans of the Hammond-Harwood House, Annapolis, Md.; this portrait is the document identifying him as the architect of the house.

Canvas 36⅝ x 27½ / 1774-87
Coll.: Harwood / Francis P. Garvan
Exh.: Lyon 1941 no. 16 / Oberlin 1946 no. 9 / Peale 1953 no. 11 / —1954 no. 9
Ref.: Sellers no. 88, 68 / —1939 / *Antiquarian* Sept. 1928 / *Bull.* June 1935 / —Feb. 1938 / Shoolman 1942 / *Antiques* June 1951 / Yale 1951 / Pierson 1960
Yale University Art Gallery (The Mabel Brady Garvan Collection 1934), New Haven, Conn.

22 HENRY CLAY (1777-1852)
Statesman

Canvas 24 x 20 / 1818 / Cf. portrait by Rembrandt at PAFA (Lewis 1934 no. 6)

Coll.: PPM (*sale* 1854 no. 134)
Exh.: Cincinnati 1852 no. 134 / Peale 1923 no. 85 / —1953 no. 16 / —1954 no. 10 / New York 1941
Ref.: Sellers no. 144, 319 / *Ky. Gaz.* 11 Dec. 1818 / HSP 1942
The Historical Society of Pennsylvania (gift of Charles S. Ogden 1896), Philadelphia

22

23 GEN. JOHN CROPPER (*1756-1821*)

Canvas 36 x 26½ / Signed and dated lower left
    C. W Peale/1792
Exh.: Peale 1953 no. 12 / 1963 no. 6
Ref.: Sellers no. 166, 250

United States National Museum, Smithsonian Institution (bequest of Mrs. John Cropper), Washington, D.C.

24 MRS. JOHN CROPPER (*1772-1855*)
    Catherine Bayly, second wife of Gen. Cropper

Canvas 36 x 27 / Signed and dated lower right
    C. W Peale 1792
Exh.: Peale 1953 no. 13 / —1963 no. 7
Ref.: Sellers no. 167, 249 / *Art Qu.* Aut. 1939

United States National Museum, Smithsonian Institution (bequest of Mrs. John Cropper), Washington, D.C.

25 GEN. HENRY DEARBORN (1751-1829)

Canvas 22⅜ x 19½ / 1796/97
Coll.: PPM (*sale* 1854 no. 155) / City of Philadelphia
(on permanent loan to INHP 1951)
Exh.: Cincinnati 1852 no. 155
Ref.: Sellers no. 189, 292
Independence National Historical Park, Philadelphia

26 MRS. GERARD DePEYSTER

Margaret DePeyster (1774-1815), married her
cousin (1776-1824); both were cousins of the artist's
second wife

p. 30 Miniature 2½ x 2 / 1798
Ref.: Sellers no. 199, 450
*The New-York Historical Society (gift of Waldron
Phoenix Belknap Jr. 1947), New York*

27 MASTER FERGUSON AS CUPID

Thomas Ladson Ferguson

Miniature 1¹⁵⁄₁₆ x 1⅜ / c. 1785 / Also attributed to
James Peale
Coll.: Mrs. Miles White Jr., Baltimore
Exh.: White 1965
Ref.: Brockway 1932 no. 21
The Henry Ford Museum, Dearborn, Mich.

28 BENJAMIN FRANKLIN (1706-90)

Printer, savant and statesman

Canvas 36 x 27 / 1789 / Enlarged variant of 1785   *p. 6*
PPM portrait at PAFA (Sellers no. 279) made for
APS but rejected / Sellers (1962) transcribes
inscription on MS on table (135 words about
lightning rod) and adds it "may well be the longest
painted inscription in any portrait." / Cf. engrav-

ing (Sellers no. 280)
Coll.: John Barclay (?)
Exh.: Phila. 1887 no. 161 / Peale 1923 no. 30 / —
  1953 no. 18 / 1954 no. 12 / MMA 1936 no. 8 /
  Washington 1937 no. 137 / —1950 no. 77 /
  Denver 1958
Ref.: Sellers no. 281, 173 / —1962 / Bowen 1892 /
  Ogg 1927 / Cahill 1935 / HSP 1942 / *NGM* Feb.
  1951 / *Bull.* Jan. 1956 / Pierson 1960
*The Historical Society of Pennsylvania (gift of James
Joseph Barclay 1852), Philadelphia*

29 FRENCH OFFICER

Sometimes called Jean Baptiste Donatien de
Vimeur, Comte de Rochambeau (1725-1807), but not
related to PPM (INHP) portrait (Sellers no. 750)

Miniature 1⅜ x 1⅛ / 1781/82 (?)
Coll.: Titian R. Peale 1908
Exh.: Peale 1923 no. 287 / —1954 no. 45 / MMA
  1927 / Washington 1932 no. 105
Ref.: Sellers no. 1014, 425 / —1939 / Bolton 1921
  no. 13 / Wehle 1927

*Museum of Art, Carnegie Institute (The Herbert
DuPuy Collection 1927), Pittsburgh*

30 ROBERT FULTON (1765-1815)

Artist and inventor / An unrelated portrait at DIA,
traditionally attributed to Rembrandt Peale, is sometimes attributed to John Vanderlyn (1775-1852)

Canvas 23½ x 19⅝ / 1807
Coll.: PPM (*sale* 1854 no. 53) / City of Philadelphia
  (on permanent loan to INHP 1951)
Exh.: Cincinnati 1852 no. 53
Ref.: Sellers no. 283, 298 / Dunlap 1918 / *Art Qu.*
  Sum. 1948

Independence National Historical Park, Philadelphia

31 NANCY HALLAM AS IMOGEN

Scene from Shakespeare's *Cymbeline*, act 3, sc. 6: Imogen disguised as boy Fidele / Nancy (or Sarah) played in Williamsburg, Charleston, Annapolis, Philadelphia and New York in 60s and early 70s. In 1774 she went to Jamaica; married John Raynard, church organist at Kingston.

Canvas 50 x 40¼ / 1771
Coll.: PPM (*sale* 1854 no. 246) / "Baird" / Marguerite Kumm
Exh.: Annapolis Theatre Oct. 1771
Ref.: Sellers no. 342 / *Time* 28 Jan. 1957
Colonial Williamsburg

32   *BENJAMIN HARRISON JR. (c. 1750-99)*
Richmond merchant (not "Signer" as once identified)

Canvas 30 x 25 / Signed and dated lower right *C. W Peale/Pinx.* 1783 / Inscribed on object in his right hand: Benjn Harrison Junr Esqr/Berkeley Jas River/Virginia
Coll.: Gwyne Page Harrison (great-grandson) / his widow / Hugh Nelson Jr. (her widower) / Thomas B. Clarke / A. W. Mellon Charitable and Educational Trust (deposited at NGA 1942 for NPG 1965)
Exh.: Union 1922 no. 9 / Richmond 1929 no. 125 / —1947 no. 12 / Clarke 1928 / Washington 1937 no. 13 / Hagerstown 1955 / Williamsburg 1951 / El Paso 1960 / Peale 1963 no. 5
Ref.: Sellers no. 364, 144 / *Am. Coll.* Sep. 1947
National Portrait Gallery, Smithsonian Institution, Washington, D. C.

33   *JOHN PAUL JONES (1747-92)*
Naval Officer

p. 22   Canvas 21 x 19 / 1781 / Used for miniature by James or his daughter Anna
Coll.: PPM (*sale* 1854 no. 42) / City of Philadelphia (on permanent loan to INHP 1951)

Exh.: Cincinnati 1852 no. 42 / Knoedler 1945 no. 2 / MMA 1948 / Peale 1954 no. 16
Ref.: Sellers no. 427, 109 / *Time* 27 Sep. 1954 / Jensen 1955 / Eliot 1957
Independence National Historical Park, Philadelphia

34   *GEN. JOHANN (BARON) DE KALB (1721-80)*
Hero of battle of Camden, S. C., 16 Aug. 1780

Canvas 22 x 18 / 1781/82 / One of three replicas of lost life portr. 1780 (Sellers no. 428-30)
Coll.: PPM (*sale* 1854 no. 25) / City of Philadelphia (on permanent loan to INHP 1951)
Exh.: Cincinnati 1852 no. 25 / Peale 1954 no. 17
Ref.: Sellers no. 431, 104 / Wood 1927
Independence National Historical Park, Philadelphia

34

35

35 LAFAYETTE

Marie Joseph Paul Yves Roch Gilbert du Motier, Marquis de Lafayette (1757-1834), French soldier and statesman

Canvas 48½ x 40 / Signed lower left *C. W Peale pinx.* 1779 / 1780/81
Coll.: George Washington
Exh.: Richmond 1929 / Washington 1932 no. 138
Ref.: Sellers 445, 102 / *Penn. Mag.* v. 28 / *Scribner's Mag.* June 1898 / Bolton 1939 / *Winterthur Portfolio I* 1964

Washington and Lee University (gift of Gen. George Washington Custis Lee), Lexington, Virginia

36 THE MARQUIS DE LA FAYETTE

Mezzotint 7⅜ x 5⅝ (paper 8¾ x 7¼) / 1787 / Inscribed with title and *Major General in the Armies of the United States of America. C. W. Peale Pinxt. et Fecit* / Probably after lost 1781 PPM portrait / The life portrait is at Washington and Lee Univ. (no. 35); there are replicas (cf. Sellers no. 445-48; 446 may be a copy). / Rembrandt did two later life portraits (cf. MMA 1965)
Ref.: Sellers no. 450 / —1933 / Stauffer 1907 no. 2424 / *Winterthur Portfolio I* 1964

The Metropolitan Museum of Art (gift of Samuel P. Avery 1894), New York

37 BENJAMIN AND ELEANOR RIDGELY LAMING

Laming (c. 1750-92), Baltimore merchant, married 1784 Eleanor (c. 1760-1829), who later married 1803 James Dall (d. 1808)

Canvas 41½ x 60 / 1788
Coll.: Ridgely / Mrs. Ridgely Palmer, Baltimore / Luke V. Lockwood, Greenwich, Conn. (*sale* New York 15 May 1954 no. 455) / Morris Schapiro, Baltimore

37

Exh.: Girl Scouts 1929 no. 834 / Peale 1954 no. 19 /
Baltimore 1958 / Washington 1960 no. 21 / MMA
1965
Ref.: Sellers no. 453, 184 / —1939 / MMA *Bull.*
Apr. 1965
*National Gallery of Art (gift of Morris Schapiro 1966),
Washington, D. C.*

38   *CHARLES ALEXANDRE LESUEUR*
(1778-1846)
French artist and naturalist

Canvas 23 x 19 / 1818 / Once attributed to Rembrandt

Coll.: PPM (*sale 1854 no. 186*)
Exh.: Cincinnati 1852 no. 186 / Peale 1923 no. 252 /
—1937 no. 30 / —1954 no. 22
Ref.: Sellers no. 476, 327 / *Mag. of Art* Apr. 1951
*The Academy of Natural Sciences of Philadelphia
(gift of George Ord 1854)*

39   *MERIWETHER LEWIS (1774-1809)*
Soldier and explorer

Panel 23 x 18¾ / 1807 / Also in 1807 for PPM,
CWP sculpted Lewis in wax and clothed it
"in an Indian dress presented to Capt. Lewis by
Comeawait, Chief of Shoshone Nation" (Sellers

39

41

no. 482).
Coll.: PPM (*sale* 1854 no. 165) / City of Philadelphia
(on permanent loan to INHP 1951)
Exh.: Cincinnati 1852 no. 165 / Peale 1954 no. 23
Ref.: Sellers no. 481, 299 / Ewers 1965
Independence National Historical Park, Philadelphia

40   TIMOTHY MATLACK (1736-1829)
Philadelphia politician, known as the "fighting
Quaker"

p. 60   Canvas 24⅛ x 20 / 1826 / It seems appropriate that
the 85 year old artist's last portrait, a double
example of longevity for his PPM, should depict
his 90 year old friend. / A younger portrait, long
attributed to CWP, is now given to Rembrandt
(no. 147)
Coll.: PPM (*sale* 1854 no. 65) / City of Philadelphia
(on permanent loan to INHP 1951)

Exh.: Cincinnati 1852 no. 65
Ref.: Sellers no. 539, 351
Independence National Historical Park, Philadelphia

41   GEN. WILLIAM MOULTRIE (1730-1805)

Canvas 26½ x 22¼ / 1782 / Enlarged replica of lost
1782 PPM portrait (copy by James B. Sword at
HSP) / Copy by Rembrandt at Carolina Art
Association / Cf. background with no. 97.
Coll.: William Moultrie Reid / Eunice Chambers /
A. W. Mellon Charitable and Educational Trust
(deposited at NGA 1942-65)
Exh.: Louisville 1947 / Asheville 1949 / Columbia
1950 / Atlanta 1951 no. 7 / Charlotte 1952 /
Chattanooga 1952 / Peale 1963 no. 3 / Raleigh 1963
Ref.: Sellers no. 584, 135 / —in *Antiques* Dec. 1954
*National Portrait Gallery, Smithsonian Institution,
Washington, D. C.*

42 MRS. JOHN NICHOLSON AND CHILD

Wife and son of John Nicholson (d. 1800), Comptroller-general of Pennsylvania and partner of Robert Morris (no. 200)

Canvas 36 x 27¼ / Signed and dated lower right
  C. W Peale/painted 1790 / The companion portrait
  is also at Chicago (Sellers no. 594).
Coll.: M. Nicholson Collins (desc.)
Exh.: Vancouver 1955 no. 7
Ref.: Sellers no. 595 / —1939 / *Bull.* Mar. 1923 /
  Chicago 1961

*The Art Institute of Chicago (gift of Mr. and Mrs.
Carter H. Harrison 1952)*

43 GEN. WILLIAM NORTH (1755-1836)

Aide-de-camp and adopted son of Baron von Steuben

Canvas 23 x 19 / 1785 / Society of the Cincinnati
  "eagle" added by another hand.
Ref.: Sellers no. 598, 169 / *Bull.* Apr. 1944 / Detroit
  1966

*The Detroit Institute of Arts (gift of Dexter M. Ferry
Jr. 1942)*

44 COL. CHARLES PETTIT (1736-1806)

Philadelphia lawyer, merchant and politician; president of Insurance Company of North America (1796-1806)

Canvas 35⅞ x 27 / Signed and dated lower left   *p. 64*
  C. W Peale/painted 1792

40   TIMOTHY MATLACK (1826) at the age of 90 by C. W. Peale at the age of 85

147   *TIMOTHY MATLACK* (1800/10) by Rembrandt Peale

47 *LT. COL. SAMUEL SMITH* (c. 1790) as commander of Fort Mifflin by C. W. Peale and James Peale. The flag shown was not the one in use during the action depicted in the background, which took place on the Delaware in the fall of 1777.

152 MAJ. GEN. SAMUEL SMITH (1816) by Rembrandt Peale. General Smith commanded the defences of the city during the Battle of Baltimore (1814) in the War of 1812.

Exh.: Peale 1923 no. 80 / —1954 no. 32 / Worcester 1929 no. 334

Ref.: Sellers no. 686, 263 / Worcester 1922 / *Art Qu.* Aut. 1939

Worcester Art Museum

45 WILLIAM PITT (1708-78)
Earl of Chatham, English statesman

p. 12 Mezzotint 23 x 14¾ / London 1768 / Signed lower right *Chas. Willson Peale pinx. et fecit.* / inscribed below *Worthy of Liberty, Mr. Pitt scorns to invade the Liberties of other People.*

Coll.: Horace Wells Sellers, Phila. (desc.; the artist's own impression)

Exh.: Oberlin 1946 no. 52 / Peale 1963 no. 59

Ref.: Sellers no. 695 / —1933 / —1939 / Stauffer 1907 no. 2426 / Hart 1915 / Halsey 1925 / Flexner 1954 / Roos 1954

Charles Coleman Sellers

46 PEYTON RANDOLPH (1721-75)
Virginia lawyer and statesman

Miniature 1½ x 1¼ / 1776 / Inscribed on back of case: Peyton Randolph, born 1721, died 1775. President of the First Continental Congress in 1774 and Delegate to Congress in 1775. Founder of Freemasonry in U.S. Painted by Charles Willson Peale / Related to 1782 PPM (INHP) portrait (Sellers no. 724)

Coll.: Titian R. Peale 1908

Exh.: Peale 1923 no. 283 / —1954 no. 46 / MMA 1927 / Washington 1932 no. 103

Ref.: Sellers no. 722, 409 / Bolton 1921 no. 10 / *Art in Am.* June 1931

Museum of Art, Carnegie Institute (The Herbert DuPuy Collection 1927), Pittsburgh

47 COL. SAMUEL SMITH (1752-1839)

Canvas 23⅜ x 19¼ / 1788/93 / Historical background probably by James / Family replica unlocated (Sellers no. 806) / Cf. Rembrandt's portrait of him as Maj. Gen. after War of 1812 (no. 152)

Coll.: PPM (*sale* 1854 no. 46) / City of Philadelphia (on permanent loan to INHP 1951)

Exh.: Cincinnati 1852 no. 46 / Peale 1923 no. 42 / —1954 no. 36

Ref.: Sellers no. 805, 199

Independence National Historical Park, Philadelphia

48 CAPT. ANDREW SUMMERS (1742-1806)
Philadelphia broker; a miniature of his son, whose son married Sybilla, the artist's daughter, is also in the DuPuy coll.

Miniature 1⅝ x 1¼ / 1782

Exh.: Peale 1923 no. 280 / — 1954 no. 47 / MMA 1927

Ref.: Sellers no. 843, 433 / Bolton 1921 no. 16 / Wehle 1927 / *Art in Am.* June 1931

Museum of Art, Carnegie Institute (The Herbert DuPuy Collection 1927), Pittsburgh

50

49   MRS. ANDREW SUMMERS
Hannah (1742-1819)

Miniature 1¾ x 1⅜ / 1782
Exh.: Peale 1923 no. 304 / — 1954 no. 48 / MMA 1927
Ref.: Sellers no. 844, 434 / Bolton 1921 no. 17 /
Country Life July 1927 / Wehle 1927 / *Art in Am.*
June 1931
*Museum of Art, Carnegie Institute (The Herbert
DuPuy Collection 1927), Pittsburgh*

50   COL. GEORGE WASHINGTON (1732-99)
First President of the United States (1789-97) /
Sat to CWP for his first portrait and for six others
(1772-95)

Canvas 17¼ x 14⅞ / 1772 / Possibly first life por-
trait, but probably replica (head only) of portrait
at Washington and Lee Univ. (Sellers no. 894);
Raphaelle or Rembrandt probably completed
(uniform) c. 1810 for PPM
Coll.: PPM (*sale* 1854 no. 271)
Exh.: Peale 1923 no. 163
Ref.: Sellers no. 895, 353 / Johnston 1882 / *McClure's
Mag.* Feb. 1897 / *Ency. Brit.* 1929 v. 23 / *Anti-
quarian* Feb. 1931 / Morgan and Fielding 1931 no.
2 / Eisen 1932 / HSP 1942 / Jensen 1955
*The Historical Society of Pennsylvania (gift of Charles
S. Ogden 1892), Philadelphia*

51   HIS EXCELLENCY GEORGE
   WASHINGTON ESQR.

Mezzotint 11⅝ x 9½ (paper 12⅝ x 9⅝) / c. 1777 /   *p. 68*
Engraved by unknown artist after Peale's second
life portrait 1776 at Brooklyn Museum (Sellers no.
896) / Colored with blue / See companion, no. 57
Exh.: MMA 1963 no. 215
Ref.: Cf. Sellers no. 903 / Sellers 1933 / Hart 1904
no. 1 / Stauffer 1907 no. 2427
*The Metropolitan Museum of Art (bequest of Charles
Allen Munn 1924), New York*

52   GEORGE WASHINGTON AT PRINCETON
Commemorates battle of Princeton 3 Jan. 1777

Canvas 52 x 49 / Replica of fourth life portrait 1779   *p. 13*
at PAFA (Sellers no. 904) / Cf. engraving, below
Coll.: Dr. Frisby Tilghman McKaig
Exh.: Cleveland 1936 no. 38 / Greensburg 1959 no. 87

Impression with letters, courtesy Henry Francis du Pont Winterthur Museum (not in exhibition) (cf. no. 54)

Ref.: Sellers no. 910, 359 / *Bull.* Feb. 1918 / Morgan and Fielding 1931 / Eisen 1932

The Cleveland Museum of Art

53   GEORGE WASHINGTON

p. 13   Mezzotint 12 x 9⅞ (plate 13⅞ x 9⅞) / Signed and dated lower left *Chas. Willson Peale Pinxt. et fecit* 1780 / Inscribed below *His Excellency George Washington Esquire, Commander in Chief of the Federal Army—/This Plate is humbly Inscribed to the Honorable the Congress of the United States of America,/by their Obedient Servant,/Chas. Willson Peale.* / Derived from life 1779 portrait (cf. no. 52) / Earliest known signed and dated engraved portrait of subject, perhaps first print showing

American flag with thirteen stars
Exh.: MMA 1963 no. 218
Ref.: Sellers no. 916 / —1933 / Hart 1904 no. 2 / Stauffer 1907 no. 2428
J. William Middendorf II

54   WASHINGTON (CONVENTION PORTRAIT)

Mezzotint 7½ x 5¾ (paper 10¾ x 8¾) / Proof before letters / Letters read *Painted & Engrav'd. by C. W. Peale. 1787./His Excel: G. Washington Esq: L.L.D. Late Commander in Chief of the Armies of the U. S. of America & President of the Convention of 1787* / After sixth life portrait 1787 at PAFA (Sellers no. 939) which was posed for expressly to be engraved; James did a miniature at the same sittings.
Ref.: Sellers no. 940 / —1933 / Hart 1904 no. 3 / Stauffer 1907 no. 2429 / *Winterthur Portfolio I* 1964
The Metropolitan Museum of Art (bequest of Charles Allen Munn 1924), New York

55   WASHINGTON

Silhouette cut-out 2⅞ h. (paper 7⅜ x 4⅛) /   *p. 89*
PEALE'S MUSEUM stamp with eagle below (see no. 111) / Inscribed below *G. Washington* / Backed with black cloth / In original frame 13¼ x 15¼ with black and gilt glass (sight 3¾ x 3) / Not identical with so-called 1794 silhouette in Hart (*McClure's Mag.* Feb. 1897), Carrick 1928, Jackson 1938
Mr. and Mrs. Walter E. Simmons

56   PRESIDENT WASHINGTON

Panel 7½ x 6 / 1795/98 / Reduced replica of seventh life portrait 1795 at NYHS (Sellers no. 942) / James, Raphaelle, and Rembrandt, for whose benefit the sittings were arranged (see no. 156), also worked at them; Gilbert Stuart had sittings on alternate days and made the pun that

Washington was being *"Pealed* all round."
Coll.: Calahan, Annapolis, Md. / Ridgely, Washington, D. C.
Ref.: Sellers no. 948 / Boston 1921 no. 761
Museum of Fine Arts, Boston (bequest of Charles Sumner 1874)

51

The Metropolitan Museum of Art (bequest of Charles Allen Munn 1924), New York

57   MRS. GEORGE WASHINGTON

Martha Dandridge Custis (1732-1802) married Washington in 1759.

Miniature 1¼ x 1¹⁄₁₆ / 1772 / Painted at Mt. Vernon when CWP did first life portrait of her husband (cf. no. 50)
Coll.: Kate Williams Upshur / Kate Upshur Moorhead
Exh.: Peale 1954 no. 50
Ref.: Sellers no. 952, 397 / Lossing 1871 / Yale 1951
Yale University Art Gallery (The Mabel Brady Garvan Collection 1947), New Haven, Conn.

58   LADY WASHINGTON

Mezzotint 11¾ x 9⅝ (paper 12⅝ x 9⅝) / c. 1777 / Print by unknown artist after lost 1776 Hancock portrait / Colored with blue / Pendant to no. 51
Exh.: MMA 1963 no. 216
Ref.: Cf. Sellers no. 953, 374 / Stauffer 1907 no. 2430

59   MARTHA WASHINGTON

Canvas 28¼ x 23½ / Pendant to 1795 life portrait

at NYHS (Sellers no. 942) / Copied by Rembrandt (no. 161)

Coll.: PPM *(sale* 1854 no. 225) / L. H. Newbold / City of Philadelphia (on permanent loan to INHP 1951)

Exh.: Cincinnati 1852 no. 225

Ref.: Sellers no. 957, 375 / MMA 1965

Independence National Historical Park, Philadelphia

60   *GEN. ANTHONY WAYNE* (1745-96)
Waged and won Northwestern Indian War

1792-95. His troops occupied Detroit before his arrival in the course of inspecting western military posts, and during his residence at Detroit in 1796 the establishment of Wayne County, Northwest Territory, was proclaimed (now, smaller, Wayne County, Mich.).

Canvas 21½ x 19 / 1783/84 / Cf. no. 162

Coll.: PPM *(sale* 1854 no. 11) / William Wayne / Mary Atlee Wayne Wirgman / Polly Wayne Kittelle

Exh.: Cincinnati 1852 no. 11

Ref.: Sellers no. 961 / Wood 1927

Private Collection

61   *GEN. OTHO HOLLAND WILLIAMS* (1749-94)

Miniature 1⁹⁄₁₆ x 1³⁄₁₆ / c. 1785 / Derived from 1782 canvas, variant of which in PPM (Sellers no. 985-86) was copied by Rembrandt for PBM (BPM 1956 no. 96)

Ref.: Sellers no. 987, 440 / MHS 1945

Maryland Historical Society (bequest of Susan Williams 1921), Baltimore

The Historical Society of Pennsylvania (gift of Charles S. Ogden 1892), Philadelphia

LANDSCAPES

63 FALLS OF THE SCHUYLKILL

Ink and watercolor 7¾ x 12¾ / c. 1770 / Inscribed above *the lower falls of the Schuylkill 5 miles from Philadelphia* / Used for background in 1770 portrait of John Dickinson at HSP (Sellers no. 217)
Exh.: Peale 1963 no. 57
Charles Coleman Sellers

64 VIEW OF WEST POINT

Watercolor 6¼ x 7⅞ / c. 1801 / Inscribed above *View of West point from the side of the mountain* / In: Hudson River Sketch Book
American Philosophical Society Library, Philadelphia

65 VIEW OF THE GARDEN AT BELFIELD

At first CWP called his estate near Germantown, where he lived 1810-21, "Farm Persevere," but later changed it to "Belfield" in remembrance of the home of his old mentor John Hesselius on the Severn in Maryland.

62 MAMOUT YARROW

A Mohammedan of Georgetown, D. C., reputedly 134 years old / Once called "Billy" Lee, Washington's manservant

Canvas 24 x 20 / 1819
Coll.: PPM *(sale* 1854 no. 262)
Exh.: Cincinnati 1852 no. 262 / Peale 1923 no. 199 / —1954 no. 26 / Oberlin 1946 no. 10
Ref.: Sellers no. 1007, 330 / HSP 1942 / —*Bull.* April 1947

64

67

65

Canvas 28¼ x 36¼ / 1816 / Copied by Rubens 1860
(list no. 48): I take great interest in copying this
picture as it represents the garden . . . [in] which
I laid out the walks and planted nearly all the
trees, shrubs & box edgings. *(Art Qu.* Sum. 1960)
Coll.: PPM *(sale* 1854) / Franklin Peale
Ref.: Sellers 1947 / Poesch 1957
Private Collection

66   BELFIELD FARM

p. 20   Canvas 10¾ x 15⅝ / 1815/20 / For other Belfield
and vicinity views, see Poesch 1957, Peale 1965
no. 43, and below.
Coll.: Augustin Runyon Peale / Ralph L. Parkinson
Exh.: Cf. PAFA 1819 no. 86
*The Detroit Institute of Arts (gift of Dr. and Mrs.
Irving Levitt 1963)*

67   MILL BANK, UPPER DARBY

View of the Sellers estate made for the artist's
son-in-law Coleman Sellers

Canvas 15 x 21 / 1815/20
Exh.: New London 1944 no. 92 / Peale 1963 no. 10
Mrs. Charles C. Sellers

OTHER WORKS

68   ELISHA RAISING THE SHUNAMMITE'S SON

2 Kings 4: 37

p. 11   Watercolor 16 x 24 / Copy 1767/68 after Benjamin
West's 1765 canvas now at the J. B. Speed Art
Museum, Louisville, Ky.
Exh.: Peale 1963 no. 58
Charles Coleman Sellers

69   FLOWERS AND FRUIT
Panel 10¾ x 13⅛

70   FRUIT

Board 10¾ x 13⅛ / Two still lifes traditionally
attributed to CWP c. 1770 on basis of confused
inscriptions on backs that they were given by Mrs.
James Gibson, daughter of John Beale Bordley
(1727-1804), to Maria Peale, daughter of James
Peale. J. B. Bordley was C. W. Peale's dearest
friend and an amateur artist who studied with
him. Sellers suggests both these still lifes may be
by Bordley, the one on panel possibly by CWP. /
Sellers lists five portraits of Bordley (Sellers no.
61-65).
Coll.: Rubens H. Peale 1925 / Mrs. Albert W. Sully
Exh.: Brooklyn Mus. 1930 no. 17664 / Levy 1941
no. 2 / Peale 1954 no. 42-43
*The Detroit Institute of Arts (gifts of Dexter M.
Ferry Jr. 1952)*

JAMES PEALE

(1749 Chestertown, Md.—
Philadelphia 1831)

was the youngest brother of C. W. Peale. He was trained as a cabinet maker and made frames for his brother's art while learning it from him. He, too, served in the Continental Army and attained the rank of captain. Until he married Mary (1782), daughter of the painter James Claypoole (1720-96), he belonged to his brother's household. James became the miniaturist of the family (in 1786 C. W. Peale and James agreed to share the portrait painting field: the elder to do oils; the younger, miniatures) until, with failing eyesight, he turned almost exclusively to still life.

Apparently he painted only two life portraits of Washington, both miniatures (1787 and 1795; see biography of Rembrandt Peale). The number of canvases he did after his brother's portraits has not been determined. In reference to the one of 1787, Charles Coleman Sellers wrote (1939):

"James used the head for a few portraits, in which he elaborated the figure and introduced a portrait of himself, in uniform, holding the bridle of the General's horse. Charles Peale Polk also took up the strain, copying the head into a half-length likeness of dubious merit, which, with occasional assistance from his relatives, he repeated over a hundred times through the succeeding years.

"While each of the three artists has thus a distinct type of Washington portrait from this sitting, it is impossible always to make a definite identification. A word might be said upon the identification of Peale portraits in general. The style, particularly of Charles Willson and James, was remarkably similar, and it has become customary to sort out their work by making positive statements based on the type or size of the painting. Doubt is an element of history, and these dicta are more flattering to the voice of authority than deserving of respect. Opinion can

184

never outweigh evidence, or the lack of it. The Peales, these brothers in particular, did not hesitate to finish or retouch one another's canvases. Furthermore, they would paint in any size that the purchaser desired, at any time in their lives, allowing only for the fact that work in miniature had to be discontinued with advancing years and failing eyesight."

Family Portraits

71   SELF-PORTRAIT

Miniature 2⅝ x 2⅛ / 1810/15 / Brockway (in. *Antiques* Oct. 1932) lists 6 self-portrait miniatures (62-67).
Coll.: Anna C. Peale / E. O. Allen / Margaretta A. Peale
Ref.: Cf. Brockway 1932 no. 62
The R. W. Norton Art Gallery, Shreveport

72 THE ARTIST AND HIS FAMILY

James with his wife, Mary Chambers Claypoole (1753-1829), and children, from left to right, Jane Ramsay (1785-1834), James Jr. (1789-1876), Maria (1787-1866), Margaretta Angelica (1795-1882), and Anna Claypoole (1791-1878)

Probably shown at Columbianum (Phila. 1795 no. 69) as *A family, small whole lengths, in Oil.*

p. 28   Canvas 30½ x 32½ / c. 1795/98
Exh.: Peale 1923 no. 108 / —1939 / —1944 no. 12 / —1953 no. 30 / —1954 no. 86 / Lewis 1934 no. 203 / Phila. 1940 no. 54 / —1944 no. 23 / Pittsburgh 1940 no. 113 / BPM 1941 no. 12 / Columbus 1947 no. 18 / Detroit 1957 no. 57
Ref.: *Art Qu.* Win. 1954 / Flexner 1954 / Jensen 1955 / Richardson 1956 / Pierson 1960
The Pennsylvania Academy of the Fine Arts (gift of John Frederick Lewis 1922), Philadelphia

73 JANE RAMSAY PEALE

The artist's oldest child (1785-1834), married 1806 Dr. Samuel Simes (d. 1813); mother of Mary Jane Simes, miniaturist (no. 218)

p. 27   Canvas 28 x 21 / c. 1802
Addison Gallery of American Art, Phillips Academy (gift from the collection of Waldron Phoenix Belknap Jr. 1958), Andover, Mass.

74 ANNA AND MARGARETTA PEALE

Sometimes identified rather as the artist's youngest daughters, Margaretta and Sarah (1800-85)

Canvas 29 x 24
Coll.: Anna Peale Amies
Exh.: Peale 1923 no. 7 / —1963 no. 14
Ref.: PAFA 1902 no. 111½
The Pennsylvania Academy of the Fine Arts, Philadelphia

75 MARGARETTA ANGELICA PEALE
The artist's fourth daughter (1795-1882)

Canvas 27 x 20¼ / 1815/20 / Inscribed on back *Margaretta Peale / by James Peale Senr.*
Exh.: Peale 1963 no. 16
Charles Coleman Sellers

76   MRS. CHARLES WILLSON PEALE

Rachel Brewer (1744-90), the artist's sister-in-law

Miniature 2 x 1⁹⁄₁₆ / Initialed and dated lower right 1790 / On reverse, enframed by braided brown hair, there is a symbolic scene of female figure mourning at a tomb.

The Art Institute of Chicago (Mary Louise Stevenson Fund 1958)

77   REMBRANDT PEALE

The artist's nephew (1778-1860), son of the above

Miniature 2⁵⁄₁₆ x 1¾ / Initialed and dated lower right 1795
Coll.: G. B. Wirgam (desc.)
Exh.: Peale 1923 no. 284 / —1954 no. 102 / Washington 1925 no. 93 / —1960 no. 28 / MMA 1927 / Brooklyn 1936 no. 213 / New Haven 1940 no. 22
Ref.: Bolton 1921 no. 43 / Wehle 1927 / —in *Country Life* July 1927 / Brockway 1932 no. 70 / *Antiques* Jan. 1941 / — June 1951 / Sellers 1947 / Yale 1951
Yale University Art Gallery (gift of Mrs. John Hill Morgan 1940), New Haven, Conn.

78   MRS. CHARLES WILLSON PEALE

Elizabeth DePeyster (1765-1804), the artist's sister-in-law

Miniature 3 x 2½ / Initialed and dated lower right 1795
Coll.: Mrs. William A. Patterson (dau.) / George W. Thomas / Edmund Bury / Linden T. Harris
Exh.: Independence Hall, Phila. 1936-66
Insurance Company of North America, Philadelphia

80

Other Portraits and Miniatures

79   *CAPT. JOHN ANSLEY (1769-1822)*

Canvas 28¾ x 24½ / Initialed and dated lower right
    1801
Coll.: Ozias Ansley
Ref.: *Art in Am.* Oct. 1933
Dr. and Mrs. Irving Levitt

80   *GEN. JOHN ARMSTRONG (1717-95)*

Miniature 2⁷⁄₁₆ x 1⅞ / c. 1803
Coll.: Alice Livingston Armstrong
Exh.: Peale 1963 no. 40
National Collection of Fine Arts, Smithsonian Institution (gift of Mrs. Henry L. Milmore 1950), Washington, D. C.

81   *PAUL BECK JR. (1757-1844)*
    Philadelphia merchant and philanthropist

Miniature 2⅝ x 2 / Initialed and dated lower left   *p. 31*
    1795
Exh.: MMA 1927 / Peale 1954 no. 100
Ref.: Bolton 1921 no. 1 / Wehle 1927 / *Bull.* Dec.
    1927 / *Art in Am.* Aug. 1931 / Brockway 1932 no. 3
Museum of Art, Carnegie Institute (The Herbert DuPuy Collection 1927), Pittsburgh

82   *ANNE ANRY PIERRE BELLON DePONT*
    (1772-1854)

Miniature 2¾ x 2¼ / Initialed and dated lower left
    1797
Coll.: Edouard Paul dePont (desc.)
Exh.: MMA 1927 / Peale 1954 no. 101
Ref.: Bolton 1921 no. 16 / Wehle 1927 / Brockway
    1932 no. 17
Museum of Art, Carnegie Institute (The Herbert DuPuy Collection 1927), Pittsburgh

82

83 MAJ. THOMAS HUMPHREY CUSHING
  (1755-1822)

Miniature 3 x 2⅜ / Initialed and dated lower left
  1799
Ref.: *Bull.* Dec. 1958
Art Association of Indianapolis, Herron Museum of
Art (gift of Josiah K. Lilly Jr. 1957)

84 MME DUBOCQ AND HER CHILDREN
  Marie Francoise Trochon de Lorriere Dubocq
(d. Phila. 1847); children (from left to right): Irenee
(later Mrs. Sheridan), Alphonse (d. aged 5), Marie
Aglae (later Mrs. James Croxall, grandmother of
donor), Marie Lucille Delphine (later Mrs. Antony
Chardon)

Canvas 51 x 41 / Initialed and dated lower center
  1807
Exh.: Peale 1954 no. 84 / Brooklyn 1957 no. 21
Ref.: *Bull.* Nov. 1947 / Louisville 1960
The J. B. Speed Art Museum (gift of Mrs. Aglae Kent
Bixby 1932), Louisville

85 GEORGE FISHER
  Pennsylvania lawyer (c. 1755-c. 1840)

Miniature 2⅞ x 2³⁄₁₆ / Initialed lower left
Exh.: Peale 1963 no. 41 / IBM 1966
National Collection of Fine Arts, Smithsonian Insti-
tution, Washington, D.C.

87

86 THOMAS GOODWIN (1770-1836)

Miniature 2⅜ x 1¾ / Initialed and dated lower right
  1795
Coll.: Francis P. Garvan

The R. W. Norton Art Gallery, Shreveport

87 MRS. JOHN McCLUNEY

Miniature 2⅝ x 2⅛ / Initialed and dated lower
  right 1794
Coll.: Henry Walters (*sale* New York 23 Apr. 1941
  no. 589) / Norvin H. Green (*sale* New York 30
  Nov. 1950 no. 221)
Exh.: Peale 1963 no. 42
Ref.: *Art in Am.* Feb. 1931 / Brockway 1932 no. 49
  / Sherman 1932

*National Collection of Fine Arts, Smithsonian Institu-
tion (Catherine Walden Myer Fund 1950), Washington, D. C.*

88 OLIVIA SIMES MORRIS

  Her husband, John Morris, was a co-founder with
CWP in 1794 of the short-lived Columbianum Fine
Arts Academy.

Canvas 28¾ x 24 / c. 1815
Exh.: Peale 1954 no. 85 / Illinois 1966
Ref.: Chicago 1961

*The Art Institute of Chicago (gift of the estate of Mary
Morley Sellers 1940)*

89 CAPT. PETER OSBORNE

Miniature 2⅜ x 1⅞ / Initialed and dated lower right
  1796

The R. W. Norton Art Gallery, Shreveport

90 NINIAN PINCKNEY (1776-1825)

Miniature 3⅛ x 2⅝ / Initialed and dated lower right
   1798
Coll.: H. McCoy Jones / R. T. H. Halsey / Francis
   P. Garvan
Ref.: Brockway 1932 no. 73
The R. W. Norton Art Gallery, Shreveport

91 EDMOND ROUVERT
   Philadelphia shipping merchant; born in France
as *des Brosses*

Canvas 30 x 25
Coll.: Mark W. Collet, Phila. (desc.)
Exh.: PAFA 1909-17 / Peale 1944 no. 21 / —1954
   no. 87 / Raleigh 1945 no. 15 / Columbus 1947
   no. 19 / —1958 no. 41 / Cincinnati 1958 no. 8 /
   Greensburg 1959 no. 91 / Santa Barbara 1961
   no. 4 / —1966 no. 10
*Santa Barbara Museum of Art (Preston Morton
Collection 1960)*

92 JANE ROUVERT

89

90

91

92

Jane Loge, wife of Edmond Rouvert

Canvas 30 x 25
Coll.: Mark W. Collet, Phila. (desc.)
Exh.: PAFA 1909-17 / Peale 1944 no. 22 / —1954
no. 88 / Raleigh 1945 no. 14 / Columbus 1947
no. 19 / —1958 no. 42 / Sarasota 1949 no. 3 /
Cincinnati 1958 no. 9 / Knoedler 1958 no. 9 /
Greensburg 1959 no. 90 / Santa Barbara 1961
no. 5 / —1966 no. 9
Santa Barbara Museum of Art (Preston Morton Collection 1960)

93   *CAPT. SIMEON TOBY (1774-1861)*

Miniature 2¾ x 2¼ / Initialed and dated lower
left 1806
Coll.: Francis P. Garvan
The R. W. Norton Art Gallery, Shreveport

94   *MRS. LEVI TYSON*

Hannah Craft (c. 1758-1830) married (1) Silas
Yerkes and (2) Tyson, well-to-do Quaker miller at
Abington near Philadelphia

Canvas 25 x 22 / 1810/20 / Inscribed and dated
lower left (spurious) *C. W. Peale* 1795
Exh.: Peale 1963 no. 8
Ref.: Argosy 1953
Charles Coleman Sellers

95   *MRS. JOHN WILSON*

Mary Stewart (or Stuart) of Bordentown, N. J.

Miniature 2⅝ x 2⅛ / Initialed and dated lower   *p. 31*
right 1797
Coll.: R. T. H. Halsey
Exh.: MMA 1927
Ref.: Halsey 1925 / Mather 1927 / Wehle 1927 /

Art in Am. Aug. 1931 / Brockway 1932 no. 100
The R. W. Norton Art Gallery, Shreveport

96   YOUNG MAN

p. 33   Miniature 2⅞ x 2¼ / Initialed and dated lower right
1813
Coll.: David B. Steinberg, Cincinnati
Munson-Williams-Proctor Institute, Utica, N.Y.

HISTORICAL PIECES

97   SIR PETER PARKER'S ATTACK AGAINST FORT MOULTRIE

p. 24   Canvas, 20¼ x 29½ / c. 1782 / Title inscribed on
back by artist with date of battle in S. C.: June 28,
1776 / Cf. background in portrait of Col. Moultrie
(no. 41)
Coll.: Francis Bailey and desc. (as with his portrait,
no. 16)
Exh.: Peale 1954 no. 90
Ref.: Sellers in *Antiques* Dec. 1954
Colonial Williamsburg

98   THE GENERALS AT YORKTOWN

From left to right: Lafayette, Washington, Henry
Knox (?), Rochambeau, Alexander Hamilton (?),
Col. Tench Tilghman, aide-de-camp

p. 24   Canvas, 20¼ x 29½ / c. 1785 / Replicas are in
Lafayette coll., France, at MHS (BPM 1956 no.
63), and in Turin (FARL). / James made views at
Yorktown, Vir., 1780 before its surrender (19 Oct.
1781), used for CWP *Washingtons* (cf. Sellers no.
919, Rochambeau coll., 1782). Portraits 1781-83
of other generals already were in PPM (Sellers
no. 440, 446, 750), except Hamilton (but see
earlier CWP miniature, Sellers no. 344-45). Poses
of Washington and Tilghman apparently were
derived from, respectively, *Washington at Princeton* (made for and at Princeton; Sellers no. 933)
and *Washington, Lafayette and Tilghman at York-*
town 1784 (made for and at Annapolis; Sellers no.
935) by CWP.
Coll. and Ref.: Same as no. 97
Exh.: Peale 1954 no. 91
Colonial Williamsburg

LANDSCAPES

99   LANDSCAPE

Pen and wash 4½ x 7 / From a sketch book   *p. 27*
American Philosophical Society Library, Philadelphia

100   PEALE'S MUSEUM

Rear view of C. W. Peale's house at Third and
Lombard, Philadelphia, showing sky-lighted portrait
gallery added in 1782. Extension to right rear was
built for "moving pictures."

Panel 5¼ x 7½ / 1784/94 / Once attributed to   *p. 21*
CWP / Copied by Rubens (no. 173)
Ref.: APS 1961
American Philosophical Society Library, Philadelphia

101   ROMANTIC LANDSCAPE

Canvas 20 x 25½ / Initialed lower right / Inscribed
on back: James Peale, 1828, painted at the age
of 77

Coll.: David David, Phila.
Exh.: Peale 1963 no. 18
Ref.: *Bull.* Dec. 1963
Washington County Museum of Fine Arts, Hagerstown, Md.

102 ON THE SCHUYLKILL

Canvas 18¾ x 26¾ / Inscribed on back: James
  Peale Ser. painted in the 82nd year of his age
  Philada. 1830
Exh.: PAFA 1830/31 (?) / Ferargil 1945 no. 16 /
  Peale 1954 no. 92
*Cincinnati Art Museum (gift of Frederic Newlin
Price 1954)*

STILL LIFES

103 STILL LIFE: FRUIT

Panel 18¾ x 25¾ / Inscribed on back with name
  of artist

Exh.: San Diego 1952 / Stanford Univ. 1953 /
  Peale 1954 no. 96 / Santa Barbara 1958 no. 46
Ref.: San Francisco 1950
M. H. de Young Memorial Museum, San Francisco

104 STILL LIFE: FRUIT

Canvas 17⅛ x 27 / c. 1820 / One of several variants;
  cf. Peale 1939 no. 4,—1941 no. 11 (*Life* 30 Mar.
  1942), Baur 1940, *Kennedy Qu.* (Oct. 1966) no.
  139. See also copies (1) by Rubens 1857, at
  Harrisburg, and (2) on velvet (Baur 1940).
Exh.: Wildenstein 1959 no. 41
Ref.: *Bull.* June 1952 / Washington 1966
*The Corcoran Gallery of Art (William A. Clark Fund
1951), Washington, D.C.*

105 STILL LIFE WITH GRAPES

Canvas 16 x 22
Coll.: Susie C. Duss, Harmony, Penn.
Exh.: Des Moines 1953 / Newark 1958 no. 29 / —
  1959 / Allentown 1960 no. 74

103

104

The Newark Museum (gift of Dr. and Mrs. Earl LeRoy Wood 1955)

106   STILL LIFE: GRAPES AND WATERMELON

Canvas 18¼ x 27⅛ / Inscribed on back with name and date 1824
Coll.: Elizabeth Van Patten
Exh.: New London 1944 no. 94 / Peale 1954 no. 98 / Hartford 1958 no. 85 / —1963 no. 34
Ref.: *Art News* 16 Nov. 1940 / *Life* 30 Mar. 1942 / Born 1947

Wadsworth Atheneum (The Ella Gallup Sumner and Mary Catlin Sumner Collection 1940), Hartford, Conn.

107   STILL LIFE: PEACHES AND GRAPES

Panel 14½ x 17¾ / Inscribed on back: Painted by / James Peale / 1824 / There is a copy by Rubens in a New York coll.

Coll.: Frank and Flora Winton, Detroit
Exh.: Detroit 1962 no. 6
Private Collection

for his many depictions of Washington derived from his uncle's 1787 "Convention" portrait (cf. no. 54). Of one in Philadelphia at the Historical Society of Pennsylvania, William Sawitzky wrote: "Based on the half-length portrait of Washington by James Peale (Independence Hall), who in turn copied the head from the life portrait by C. W. Peale, 1787 (Pennsylvania Academy)." (HSP *cat.* 1942)

Polk sought portrait commissions in Philadelphia, Baltimore, and Richmond, and did not hesitate to obtain the assistance of his uncles and cousins to "improve" his work. He was married three times and had fifteen children. By 1818 Polk had become a government clerk in Washington and quit painting. (See also biography of James Peale.)

108   WILLIAM MOORE OF BALTIMORE

Canvas 35¼ x 28 / Signed and dated lower left
  C. Polk pinx/1793
The Henry Ford Museum, Dearborn, Mich.

55

109   GEORGE WASHINGTON (1732-99)

Miniature 13⁄16 x 5⁄8 / Initialed below *C.P.P.* / Black and white silhouette profile facing left / Probably derived from so-called C. W. Peale cut-out silhouette of 1794 (cf. Hart in *McClure's Mag.* Feb. 1897) / Cf. no. 55
Coll.: Mrs. Miles White Jr., Baltimore
Exh.: White 1965
The Henry Ford Museum, Dearborn, Mich.

CHARLES PEALE POLK

(1767 Maryland—Washington, D.C. 1822)

was the orphan son of C. W. Peale's sister Elizabeth Digby Peale Polk, wife of Capt. Robert Polk (killed in naval action 1777). He was raised and trained by his uncle. Like his cousin Rubens, most of his original works have a primitive "air," but he is best known

110

RAPHAELLE PEALE

(1774 Annapolis, Md.— Philadelphia 1825)

was the eldest son of C. W. Peale to survive infancy. Probably the best artist in the family, personally he was popular—for he liked to drink—but his art was not. Early he collaborated on portraits with his father, his older cousin Charles Peale Polk, and younger brother Rembrandt. With the latter he tried unsuccessfully to establish a museum in Baltimore (1797-99). He was financially successful only briefly (1803-5) in exploiting the "physiognotrace" (profile making machine) all around the country. In his later years, like his uncle James, he devoted himself almost exclusively to still lifes, noted for their "skill and wit."

"Raphaelle has been called the founder of the art of still life painting in America. Laughing in the face of tragedy and woe, striving toward perfect arrangement and illusion with an intuitive intensity, he will always be considered by many the greatest of the Peales." (Sellers in Peale 1963)

John Isaac Hawkins an English inventor living in Philadelphia, invented the physiognotrace in 1802, and gave the patent rights to his friend C. W. Peale, who set up one in his Philadelphia museum.

(A portrait of Hawkins by Rembrandt Peale was shown at PAFA 1842 no. 8, and he was listed in the catalog as "inventor of the Everpoint Pencil, the Physiognotracer, the Polygraph, the Claviola, &c. &c.")

Visitors to the museum could operate the physiognotrace themselves or, for a few cents, have Moses Williams, a mulatto slave, do it for them. (Williams made 8,800 silhouettes in 1803 alone, and eventually became so affluent from this activity that he was freed and married his former master's white cook.) Raphaelle may have had as many as 100,000 sitters for silhouettes on his tour with the machine (he called it a "facietrace"), and later it was featured at the New York museum as well as at the ones in Philadelphia and Baltimore. Raphaelle may not have made the silhouettes listed below, but they are placed there because he early exploited them.

110 CHARLES WILLSON PEALE (1741-1827)

Silhouette cut-out 2¾ h. (paper 5 x 4⅛) / Inscribed lower left *C. W. Peale* / Not stamped / There are variants.

The Detroit Institute of Arts (gift of Dr. and Mrs. Irving Levitt 1966)

111 RAPHAELLE PEALE (1774-1825)

Silhouette cut-out 2¾ h. (paper 5 x 4⅛) / MUSEUM stamped below / Inscribed lower right *Raphelle Peale* / There are variants / Two other stamps are also found: PEALE'S MUSEUM with a spread eagle above, and PEALE; none has been definitely associated with any specific museum; all have been used fraudulently or faked. (See C.C. Sellers in *Am. Coll.* May 1948.)

The Detroit Institute of Arts (gift of Dr. and Mrs. Irving Levitt 1966)

112 RUBENS PEALE

The artist's younger brother (1784-1865)

Watercolor 3¾ x 2⅝ / c. 1810 / Inscribed on back

A. C. Peale from J. B. Peale; drawn and painted by Raphael Peale. It is a likeness of Rubens Peale
Coll.: Albert Charles Peale
Exh.: New London 1944 no. 102 / Peale 1959 no. 33 / —1963 no. 49 / Washington 1960 no. 41 / IBM 1966
Ref.: Bury in *Am. Coll.* Aug. 1948
National Collection of Fine Arts, Smithsonian Institution (gift of Dr. Edwin Kirk 1941), Washington, D.C.

OTHER PORTRAITS AND MINIATURES

113 ROBERT BERRETT

Canvas 28¼ x 24¼ / c. 1800
Exh.: Kansas City 1953
Nelson Gallery and Atkins Museum (gift of Mr. and Mrs. Morris B. Hansell 1951), Kansas City, Mo.

114 MRS. ROBERT BERRETT
Lydia Wallace, wife of the above

Canvas 28½ x 24⅜ / c. 1800
Exh.: Kansas City 1953
Nelson Gallery and Atkins Museum (gift of Mrs. Edmund Maurice Hansell 1949), Kansas City, Mo.

115 ANDREW ELLICOTT JR.

Miniature 2¾ x 2³⁄₁₆ / Signed and dated lower left *Rape. Peale* 1801 / Inscribed inside case: R. Webb, Phila. 1801
Ref.: Bury in *Am. Coll.* Aug. 1948
Museum of Fine Arts, Boston (Ellen Kelleran Gardener Fund 1964)

116 MAJ. JAMES FERGUSON (1769-1855)

Miniature 2⅝ x 2
Exh.: Peale 1959 no. 28 / Washington 1960 no. 44
Ref.: MHS 1945
Maryland Historical Society (gift of Mrs. Charles Brantingham 1914), Baltimore

116 *118*

119 *121*

117 ROBERT KENNEDY

Miniature 3½ x 2¾ / Initialed and dated center
  right 99
Exh.: Peale 1959 no. 38
Ref.: Bury in *Am. Coll.* Aug. 1948 / Yale 1951
*Yale University Art Gallery (The Mabel Brady Garvan
Collection 1936), New Haven, Conn.*

118 MAN IN GRAY COAT

Miniature 2¾ x 2¼ / Signed lower left *R. Peale* /

Dated lower right 1819
Coll.: William Harvey Sutton / Mrs. Howard
  Conaway, Cardington, Ohio
Exh.: Peale 1959 no. 30
*Milwaukee Art Center Collection (gift of Mrs. William
H. Marshall 1958)*

119 ROBERT OLIPHANT

Miniature 2¹⁵⁄₁₆ x 2⁵⁄₁₆ / Initialed lower left and dated
  lower right 1799
Coll.: William S. Ridgely

122

Exh.: New London 1944 no. 101 / Peale 1959 no. 34 /
—1963 no. 48 / IBM 1966
Ref.: Bury in *Am. Coll.* Aug. 1948
National Collection of Fine Arts, Smithsonian Institution (gift of Bertha Jacques 1942), Washington, D.C.

120 BENJAMIN FRANCIS PEARCE
Son of Henry Ward Pearce

Miniature 2⅝ x 2⅛ / Signed and dated lower left
Raphaelle Peale 1801 / Inscribed lower right *Aged
21* / —on back of frame: In Memory of Benjamin
F. Pearce, who died at Sea Sept. 12th, 1802, Aged
22 Years
Coll.: Francis P. Garvan / Mrs. Robert Hale Bancroft / Emily Carroll Bancroft, Beverly, Mass.
Exh.: MMA 1927 / —1939-40 no. L.38.20.5/4
Ref.: Wehle 1927 / Bury in *Am. Coll.* Aug. 1948
The R. W. Norton Art Gallery, Shreveport

121 HENRY WARD PEARCE

Miniature 2½ x 2 / Signed and dated lower left
Raphe. Peale/1801 / Inscribed lower right *AE 64*
/ —on back: Henry Ward Pearce of Poplar Neck,
Cecil County, Maryland, born 2 December 1736
—died 16 January 1828

Coll., Exh. and Ref.: same as above
The R. W. Norton Art Gallery, Shreveport

122 CAPT. DOYLE E. SWEENEY
Also called McSweeney (d. 1847)

Miniature 2¾ x 2¼ / Once attributed to Rembrandt
Coll.: James L. Foote (*sale* Slatington, Penn. 22 Feb.
1907)
Exh.: Brooklyn 1917 no. 179 / MMA 1927 / Peale
1959 no. 23
Ref.: Pratt 1917 no. 64 / Bolton 1921 no. 4 /
Wehle 1927 / MMA *Bull.* Mar. 1927 / Bury in
Am. Coll. Aug. 1948
*Amherst College (bequest of Herbert Lee Pratt 1945),
Amherst, Mass.*

123 YOUNG MAN

Miniature 3⅛ x 2⅝ / Initialed and dated lower left   *p. 32*
1803
Exh.: MMA 1927 / Peale 1954 no. 67 / —1959 no. 24
Ref.: Wehle 1927 / *Bull.* Dec. 1927 / Bury in *Am.
Coll.* Aug. 1948
*Museum of Art, Carnegie Institute (The Herbert
DuPuy Collection 1927), Pittsburgh*

STILL LIFES

124 AFTER THE BATH

The most famous, and perhaps the most beautiful,
trompe l'oeil in American art; a witty still life of a
textile variously identified as a napkin, sheet or
towel. "The subject has made it popular. What
makes it a good picture is the intensity with which
the light upon the white linen has been 'realized' (to
use Cezanne's word)." (Richardson 1956)

Canvas 29 x 24 / Signed and dated lower right   *p. 37*
Raphaelle Peale 1823/*Pinxt*
Exh.: Hartford 1935 no. 29 / —1938 no. 86 / Paris
1938 no. 130 / Pittsburgh 1940 no. 67 / Santa

Barbara 1941 no. 91 / MOMA 1943 no. 2 / New London 1944 no. 99 / Denver 1948 no. 19 / Saginaw 1948 no. 44 / Wildenstein 1953 no. 11 / —1957 / Peale 1954 no. 63 / —1959 no. 10 / Penn. 1955 no. 10 / Detroit 1957 no. 60 / Washington 1959 no. 2 / St. Louis 1964 no. 8 / Whitney 1966 no. 213

Ref.: Ringel 1932 / Cahill 1935 / Soby 1935 / Burroughs 1936 / Walker 1943 / Richardson 1944 / —1956 / Born 1947 / Kansas City 1949 / Larkin 1949 / Barker 1950 / Sterling 1952 / Frankenstein 1953 / *Art Qu.* Win. 1954 / Roos 1954 / Jensen 1955 / Richardson 1956 / *Time* 24 Dec. 1956 / Eliot 1957 / Janson 1957 / Mendelowitz 1960 / Pierson 1960 / Upjohn 1963 / Green 1966

Nelson Gallery and Atkins Museum (Nelson Fund 1934), Kansas City, Mo.

125 A DECEPTION

Card rack; note especially museum ticket.

Ink and pencil 16 x 10¾ / Inscribed on back with notations by various desc. owners incl.: This done by pencil & India Ink by Raphaelle Peale, Phila, 1802

Coll.: Martha Ann Peale (wife) / Rubens Peale (son) / Franklin Peale (son) / Robert R. Peale (son) 1902 / Calvin W. Stillman, Chicago / J. W. Middendorf II, New York

Exh.: Milwaukee 1956 no. 42 / Detroit 1957 no. 61 / Peale 1959 no. 17

Kennedy Galleries Inc.

126 STILL LIFE WITH CAKE

Panel 9½ x 11½ / Signed and dated lower right *Raphaelle Peale Janry 1st* 1822
Coll.: A. E. Rueff
Exh.: Brooklyn 1944 / Peale 1953 no. 9 / Knoedler 1954 no. 34 / Milwaukee 1956 no. 43 / Washington 1960 no. 42

Ref.: Baur 1940 / Larkin 1949 / Barker 1950 / Brooklyn 1953 no. 34 / *Time* 15 Oct. 1956 / Eliot 1957 / UP 1965 MH38
The Brooklyn Museum

127 STILL LIFE WITH CELERY AND WINE

Canvas 12⅜ x 17⅛ / Signed and dated lower right *Raphaelle Peale* 1816
Munson-Williams-Proctor Institute, Utica, N.Y.

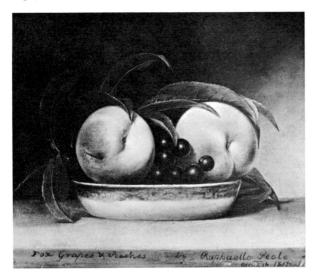

*128   STILL LIFE: FOX GRAPES AND
        PEACHES*

Panel 9¾ x 11½ / Inscribed below *Fox Grapes &
Peaches by Raphaelle Peale/August 1815*
Exh.: PAFA 1816 / BPM 1941 no. 4 / Peale 1944
no. 30 / —1959 no. 11 / —1963 no. 23 / Phila.
1944 no. 25 / Columbus 1947 no. 21
Ref.: Cook 1888 / PAFA 1902 no. 112 / *Am. Coll.*
Aug. 1946 / Born 1947
*The Pennsylvania Academy of the Fine Arts (pur-
chased from the artist), Philadelphia*

129   STILL LIFE WITH HERRING

Panel 10⅛ x 15 / Signed and dated lower right
Raphaelle Peale Feby 22, 1815/*Philadelphia*
Exh.: PAFA 1815 no. 98 / PBM 1822 no. 126 /
San Francisco 1949 / BPM 1956 no. 64 /Allentown
1959 no. 78 / Peale 1959 no. 5 / Louisville 1961
Ref.: HSP 1942 / Born 1947 / Frankenstein 1953
*The Historical Society of Pennsylvania (deposited by
Oliver Hopkinson 1891), Philadelphia*

130   STILL LIFE: LEMONS AND SUGAR

Panel 12 x 15½ / c. 1822 / Spurious inscription
lower left *R. Peale*/1847
Ref.: *Antiques* Nov. 1964
The Reading Public Museum and Art Gallery

131   STILL LIFE WITH STEAK

Panel 13⅜ x 19½ / c. 1817 / Signed lower right   *p. 38*
Painted by Raphaelle Peale
Exh.: PAFA 1817 no. 85(?) / —1829 no. 161(?) /
Providence 1954 / Peale 1954 no. 61 / —1959 no. 9
/ Rochester 1965 no. 54
Ref.: *Art Qu.* Win. 1954
Munson-Williams-Proctor Institute, Utica, N.Y.

132   STILL LIFE (WITH VEGETABLES)

Panel 11¾ x 15 / c. 1817 / Signed lower right
Raphe. Peale Pixt.
Exh.: PAFA 1817 no. 67(?) / Hartford 1942 no. 19 /
New London 1944 no. 100 / AFA 1953 / Peale
1959 no. 22
Ref.: Born 1947
*Wadsworth Atheneum (The Ella Gallup Sumner and
Mary Catlin Sumner Collection 1942), Hartford, Conn.*

133 STILL LIFE WITH WATERMELON

p. 37 Canvas 24⅜ x 29½ / Signed and dated lower right
    Raphaelle Peale 1822
Coll.: Milton Horn / Guy Fuguet, New York
Exh.: Springfield 1935 / Peale 1954 no. 62 / —1959
    no. 16 / Greensburg 1959 no. 95
Ref.: *Bull.* June 1936 / Born 1947

*Museum of Fine Arts, Springfield, Mass. (The James
Philip Gray Collection 1935)*

134 STILL LIFE WITH WINEGLASS

Panel 10¼ x 13⅝ / Signed and dated lower right   *p. 37*
    Raphaelle Peale Pinxt. A.D 1818
Exh.: PAFA 1819 no. 79(?) / Detroit 1945 no. 40 /
    Peale 1954 no. 55 / Vancouver 1955 no. 11
Ref.: Baur 1940 / *Bull.* Apr. 1944 / Richardson 1944
    / Born 1947 / Flexner 1954 / MMA 1965

*The Detroit Institute of Arts (Laura H. Murphy
Fund 1939)*

Page 100

226

132

REMBRANDT PEALE

(1778 near Richboro, Bucks County, Pa.—
Philadelphia 1860)

was the second surviving son and favorite pupil of
C. W. Peale. Together with his brothers he was an
assistant in his father's "portrait factory." When
quite young he worked in South Carolina and Maryland (and is said to have made ten replicas of his
1795 portrait of Washington in Charleston, S.C.).
He and his brother Rubens took one of the two
mastodon skeletons their father had discovered for
exhibition to London, where he also studied under
Benjamin West (1802-3). He painted portraits of
"distinguished men" for Peale's Philadelphia Museum
in Washington, New York, Boston, and Paris, where
he perhaps studied briefly with Jacques Louis David

and Francois Gerard (1801-11). In 1814 he estab-
lished Peale's Museum and Gallery of Fine Arts in
Baltimore. At his Baltimore museum Rembrandt
demonstrated the advantages of using gas for
lighting, and was a founder in 1816 of the Gas Light
Company of Baltimore (now Baltimore Gas &
Electric Co.), the first commercial gas company in
America.

In New York he became president of the expiring
American Academy of Fine Arts (succeeding Trumbull) and was a founder of the National Academy of
Design (1826). Later he worked and traveled in
Europe (1828-30) and England (1832-34), and then
settled permanently in Philadelphia. Among his ten
children there were three sets of twins and only two
sons.

He painted Washington from life but once, but in later life made a cult of his idealized "porthole" portrait, repeating it numerous times, and capitalizing on the fact that he was the last surviving artist to whom Washington had sat.

In a frequently delivered lecture on "Washington and his Portraits," Rembrandt Peale himself said (as quoted by T. Bolton and H. L. Binsse in *Antiquarian* Feb. 1931):

"It was in the autumn of 1795 that, at my father's request, Washington consented to sit to me—and the hour appointed was 7 o'clock in the morning . . . I enjoyed the rare advantage of studying the dismal countenance whilst in familiar conversation with my father. He could not sit the next day, Mrs. Washington informing me that he was engaged to sit to Mr. Stuart . . . Washington gave me three sittings. At the first and the second my father's painting and mine advanced well together, being at my right hand *his* was a little less full than *mine*. In the third sitting, perceiving that he was beginning to repaint the forehead and proceed downwards, as was his custom, I feared he would have too little time to study the mouth and lower part of the face, and therefore I began at the chin and proceeded upwards. . . . To profit more fully by the occasion, my Uncle James Peale, during the second and third sittings, painted at my left hand, a miniature on ivory, and for a time, my elder brother stood beyond my Uncle to make a profile sketch. Mrs. Washington happened to enter the room at the moment, and being amused by the circumstances, mentioned it to Stuart, who jocularly told her she must take good care of her husband, as he was in danger of being *Pealed* all round."

Charles Henry Hart wrote about the subsequent portholes in *McClure's Magazine* (Feb. 1897): "Rembrandt Peale's familiar portrait of Washington is a composite picture painted in 1823, concerning which he says, in a letter to the writer, September 24, 1860, nine days before his death: 'Besides having painted thirty-nine copies of my father's Washington, I have made seventy-nine copies of my own.' "

FAMILY PORTRAITS

135 CANDLELIGHT SELF-PORTRAIT

Canvas 55 x 45 / c. 1815 / Initialed lower left / Raphaelle and/or Rubens may have had a hand in it. / Sometimes identified as a self-portrait c. 1795, which is more likely to be a work at Wadsworth Atheneum, this portrait seems to be closer to c. 1815 when Rembrandt again had eye-trouble.
Exh.: Detroit 1962 no. 8 / Peale 1965 no. 8
Ref.: *Crayon* June 1856 (?)
The Detroit Institute of Arts (gift of the Founders Society Director's Fund 1959)

136 SELF-PORTRAIT

Canvas 19 x 14¼ / Inscribed on back: Rembrandt Peale/painted by himself/Boston 1828/for his wife Eleanor Peale. / There are other self-portraits at Amherst, Baltimore, Hartford, HSP and PAFA (cf. Peale 1923 no. 27, 60, 158, 162, 262 and—1965 no. 14, 29)
Coll.: Grafton B. Wirgman, East Orange, N. J.
Exh.: Peale 1923 no. 261 / —1941 no. 6 / —1965 no. 27 / NAD 1942 no. 13 / Minneapolis 1963 no. 94
Ref.: *Art Qu.* Aut. 1945 / Richardson 1956 / Pierson 1960 / Detroit 1966
The Detroit Institute of Arts (gift of Dexter M. Ferry Jr. 1945)

137 CHARLES WILLSON PEALE
The artist's father (1741-1827)

Chalk drawing heightened with white 20½ x 15½
Kennedy Galleries Inc.

137

138   CHARLES WILLSON PEALE

Only known oil portrait of CWP by his son / The elder Peale's 1805 and 1818 portraits of Rembrandt are unlocated (Sellers no. 665-66)

Canvas 29¾ x 24½ / 1812 / Inscribed center right:
   C. W. Peale AE 71/by Rembrandt Peale
Coll.: Rosalba C. Peale (dau.)
Exh.: Peale 1937 no. 44 / Peale 1965 no. 19
Ref.: HSP 1942 / Jensen 1955
The Historical Society of Pennsylvania (bequest of Mrs. John J. Henry 1935), Philadelphia

139   RUBENS PEALE WITH A GERANIUM

The artist's younger brother (1784-1865) with the first geranium brought to America

Canvas 28 x 24 / Signed and dated lower right *Rem*

Peale/1801
Coll.: Mrs. Sabin W. Colton Jr. / Mrs. Robert P. Esty, Ardmore, Penn. / Lawrence A. Fleischman, Detroit
Exh.: Peale 1923 no. 73 / —1960 no. 74 / —1965 no. 16 / Penn. 1955 no. 11 / MMA 1963 no. 185 / —1965
Ref.: Sellers 1947 / Jensen 1955 / BPM 1956 no. 82 / MMA *Bull.* Apr. 1965
Mrs. Norman B. Woolworth

140   MRS. REMBRANDT PEALE

Eleanor May Short (1776-1836), the artist's first wife

Canvas 28¼ x 23½ / c. 1815
Coll.: Eleanor Peale Davis, Phila. / Joseph Katz, Baltimore

Exh.: Peale 1923 no. 54 / —1965 no. 15 / Baltimore
1945 no. 36 / Amherst 1950
Ref.: Burroughs 1936
*Amherst College (gift of Edward S. Whitney 1949),
Amherst, Mass.*

141 ROSALBA AND ELEANOR PEALE

The artist's daughters. Rosalba Carriera (1799-
1874), artist, married 1860 John A. Underwood, also
an artist; Eleanor (1805-77) married 1825 Thomas
H. Jacobs.

Canvas 42 x 32¾ / Inscribed on back (before lining):
Rosalba Peale (in black) and her sister Eleanor
Jacobs, painted by Rembrandt Peale, N. York
1826.
Coll.: Grafton B. Wirgman, East Orange, N. J.

(desc.) / Mrs. Millicent H. Rogers (*sale* New York
8 May 1947 no. 63)
Exh.: Peale 1941 no. 4
Ref.: *Life* 30 Mar. 1942
Mr. and Mrs. F. Palmer Hart

142 MRS. REMBRANDT PEALE

Harriet Cany (c. 1800-69), the artist's second wife

Canvas 30 x 25
Exh.: Peale 1963 no. 31
David David Inc.

OTHER PORTRAITS AND MINIATURES

143 LORD BYRON

142

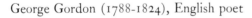

George Gordon (1788-1824), English poet

Lithograph 9¾ x 8⅜ (paper 12 x 8¾) / c. 1827 / Inscribed lower left *R. Peale del* / —lower right *Litho. of Pendleton* / Variant facing right is presumed to be earlier. (Peale 1963 no. 95) / After Richard Westall; Sully painted portrait after Westall about the same time.
Exh.: PBM 1827 (?) / Peale 1963 no. 96
The Metropolitan Museum of Art (Dick Fund 1923), New York, N.Y.

144   JOHN CALDWELL CALHOUN (1782-1850)
Statesman and political philosopher

Charcoal 18 x 14 / c. 1838 / Cf. no. 145
Exh.: Peale 1937 no. 4 / —1963 no. 78
Charles Coleman Sellers

145 *JOHN CALDWELL CALHOUN*

Canvas 30¼ x 25⅛ / 1838 / Cf. no. 144
Coll.: Mrs. Armistead Burt (niece) / Mrs. Thomas
Frost (niece) / Eugenia Calhoun Frost (dau.)
Ref.: Letter J. C. Calhoun to A. Burt 17 Nov. 1838
(Duke Univ. Lib.)

*Carolina Art Association, Gibbes Art Gallery (bequest
of Mrs. Thomas Frost 1959), Charleston, S.C.*

146 *WASHINGTON IRVING (1783-1859)*
American author

p. 32 Miniature 2¼ x 1¾ / c. 1830
The R. W. Norton Art Gallery, Shreveport

147 *TIMOTHY MATLACK (1736-1829)*
See no. 40

p. 61 Canvas 30⅛ x 25½ / Until recently attributed to
CWP
Coll.: Martha Matlack Bryan / Rebecca Bryan
Schott / Martha Bryan Schott Whitney, Phila.
(desc.; deposited HSP) / James S. Whitney /
C. K. Johnson, Greenwich, Conn. / Thomas B.
Clarke
Exh.: Union 1924 no. 4 / Clarke 1928 no. 88 /
Phila. 1955 no. 4
Ref.: Sellers no. 538, 103 / —1939 / HSP 1872 no. 9
/ *Am. Mag. of Art* June 1928 / Mendelowitz 1960
/ Green 1966

*National Gallery of Art (Andrew Mellon Collection),
Washington, D.C.*

148 *MRS. HANNAH MORE (1745-1833)*
English religious writer (not to be confused with
the artist's stepmother)

Lithograph 11 x 9½ (paper 23 x 16½) / c. 1827 /
Imprinted lower left *R. Peale del.* / —lower right
Lith. of Pendleton, Boston
Exh.: PBM 1827 / BPM 1956 no. 81 / Peale 1963
no. 94

Library of Congress, Washington, D.C.

145 (detail)

149 *ROBERT OWEN (1771-1858)*
Welsh philanthropist, founder of Socialism in
America (active at New Harmony, Ind. c. 1825)

Crayon 15⁷⁄₁₆ x 11⅞ / Initialed lower right / Inscribed
below *Robert Owen—a study from life—London
1833*
Coll.: Artist (*sale* 1862 no. 39) / Dr. Gilbert S.
Parker (cf. *sale* New York 19 Mar. 1936 no. 3) /
Erskine Hewitt (*sale* 18 Oct. 1938 no. 556)
Exh.: PAFA 1862 suppl. no. 679 / Peale 1923 no.
277 / NYHS 1935 / AFA 1965 no. 41
Ref.: *Am. Coll.* Oct. 1941 / Slatkin 1947 / Karolik
1962 no. 610

Museum of Fine Arts, Boston (M. and M. Karolik Collection 1956)

150 JOHN B. PENDLETON (1798-1866)

He and his brother William S. Pendleton helped install gas lighting at PPM and PBM in 1816. In 1820 he managed tour of *Court of Death* (no. 167), and in 1825 took up commercial lithography at Boston, publishing work by and after the Peales as well as other artists.

Canvas 30 x 25 / c. 1825
Exh.: Dallas 1941
Ref.: *Bull.* Sep. 1944, Aut. 1959
The Toledo Museum of Art (gift of Florence Scott Libbey 1941), Toledo, Ohio

151 HENRY ROBINSON

Largest stockholder in PBM; "founder of the Boston Gas Works" (PAFA)

Canvas 27 x 22 / c. 1816 / Another version is said to be dated 1849 (FARL)
Exh.: PAFA 1844 no. 74 / Peale 1923 no. 231 / —1960 no. 76 / —1965 no. 25
Ref.: *Bull.* Jan. 1965
Washington County Museum of Fine Arts, Hagerstown, Md.

152 GEN. SAMUEL SMITH

See no. 47

Canvas 37½ x 30½ / Commissioned by the City of   *p. 63*
Baltimore 1816
Exh.: Peale 1937 no. 57 / —1954 no. 75 / —1963 no. 27 / —1965 no. 20 / New York 1940 no. 184 / BPM 1956 no. 86
Ref.: BPM 1964
The Trustees of the Municipal Museum of Baltimore Inc., The Peale Museum (City Hall Collection)

153 RICHARDSON STUART (1748-1822)

Baltimore manufacturer

Canvas 20⅝ x 14⅝
Coll.: Jacob Douglas (brother-in-law) / Rebecca Douglas Hazlett / Douglas Hazlett (cf. *sale* Phila. 5 Feb. 1920 no. 25) / Thomas B. Clarke
Exh.: PBM 1823 no. 127 / Union 1921 no. 3 / Century 1926 no. 11 / Clarke 1928 no. 91 / BPM 1956 no. 88
National Gallery of Art (Andrew Mellon Collection 1947), Washington, D.C.

154 FRANCOIS JOSEPH TALMA (1763-1826)

French actor

Pencil 7¹⁵⁄₁₆ x 5¹⁵⁄₁₆ / Signed lower right *Rembrandt Peale* / Inscribed below *Original Sketch of Talma/ Paris* 1810
Exh.: Baltimore 1945 no. 32
Ref.: Baltimore 1956 no. 96
Walters Art Gallery, Baltimore

153

154

155   *BERTEL THORWALDSEN (1768-1844)*
  Danish sculptor

Canvas 26 x 18 / Painted in Rome 1829/30
Coll.: Waldemar de Raasloff / Harold de Raasloff /
Randolph Harrison Blain
*Washington and Lee University (gift of Mary Randolph
Blain in memory of Daniel Blain 1934), Lexington,
Virginia*

156   *GEORGE WASHINGTON (1732-99)*
  See no. 56

Canvas 15¼ x 11⅜ (mounted on canvas 21 x 17) /   *p. 18*
  "The original study from life, painted in Phila-
  delphia in the autumn of 1795." (W. Sawitzky in
  HSP 1942)

160

159

Exh.: Peale 1937 no. 67

Ref.: Morgan and Fielding 1931 / *Antiques* Feb. 1938 / HSP 1942 / Jensen 1955

The Historical Society of Pennsylvania (bequest of Mrs. John J. Henry 1935), Philadelphia

157 GEORGE WASHINGTON
The Gadsden-Morris-Clarke Portrait

p. 19 Canvas 29¼ x 25 / One of 10 replicas of the above done in Charleston, S.C. in 1795 / Sometimes confused with De Saussure Portrait, another S.C. replica, also once owned by T. B. Clarke (1928 no. 93), now at NPG (A. W. Mellon coll.)

Coll.: Gen Christopher Gadsden, Charleston, S.C. and desc. / Charles Henry Hart / Thomas B. Clarke (*sale* New York 1919 no. 41) / Senator James Couzens, Detroit

Exh.: Brooklyn 1917 no. 71 / Peale 1923 no. 157 / —1965 no. 9

Ref.: Morgan and Fielding 1931 / Eisen 1932 / *Bull.* Aut. 1961 / Detroit 1966

The Detroit Institute of Arts (gift of Mrs. James Couzens 1961)

158 WASHINGTON

Lithograph 20⅜ x 16¾ (paper) / 1827 / Imprinted lower left *Drawn on Stone by Rembrandt Peale.* / —lower right *Lith. of Pendleton, 9 Wall St.* / —below *Washington / From the Original Portrait Painted by Rembrandt Peale.* / "This won a silver medal from Franklin Institute, Phila., 1827. The stone was ruined accidentally when only a few impressions were taken, so this print is incredibly scarce today." (Comstock 1950) / A *p. 20*

"full blown" porthole (enframement, etc.) litho-
graph of the "National Portrait: Patriae Pater"
was also published by Pendleton in 1827 (19 x 15;
Peale 1965 no. 13). / See biography of Rosalba.
Ref.: Dunlap 1834 / —1918 / Comstock 1950
Library of Congress, Washington, D.C.

159 *WASHINGTON BEFORE YORKTOWN*

Canvas 23¾ x 19½ / Signed lower left *R. Peale* /
Inscribed on back (before lining): Painted by
Rembrandt Peale 1850 / Reduction for a print
(not made) of 13 ft. 1823 equestrian group at
Corcoran Gall. (*cat.* 1966) or oval replica (Washington only) at INHP, and 6 ft. 1823 "National
Portrait and Standard Likeness" (for head and
decorative enframement) in U.S. Capitol (replica
at PAFA; Peale 1923 no. 129) / Rembrandt and
Harriet did some 70 standard bust portholes
(36 x 29) of Washington, usually in uniform, but
sometimes in civilian dress as in original at U.S.
Capitol (cf. MMA 1965); see no. 161. / For other
equestrian Washingtons by or attributed to Rembrandt, see Cornell study (Rousuck 1947 no. 7)
and Randall-Lowndes canvas at Hammond-
Harwood House, Annapolis (BPM 1956 no. 94),
which is related to so-called CWP or James Peale
of 1795 or later at Mt. Vernon (FARL).
Exh.: PAFA 1862 suppl. no. 727
Ref.: Artist's *sale* PAFA 18 Nov. 1862 no. 96
James Graham and Sons Inc.

160 *WASHINGTON*

Lithograph 25⁵⁄₁₆ x 19⅛ (paper 39⁹⁄₁₆ x 25⅜) /
Imprinted lower left *R. Peale* / —lower right
Duval & Co. / —below *Washington / Drawn by
Rembrandt Peale from his Original Portrait/Copy
Right secured* 1856
Exh.: Peale 1963 no. 99
Ref.: Mather 1927
Library of Congress, Washington, D.C.

161 *MARTHA WASHINGTON*
See no. 59

Canvas 35¾ x 28⅝ / Signed lower left *Rembrandt
Peale* / Inscribed on back: Martha Washington,
painted by Rembrandt Peale—1858, from the
Original by C. W. Peale—1795
Coll.: Thomas Thompson, Boston (*sale* New York
7 Feb. 1870 no. 608)
Ref.: Lewis 1875 no. 433 / Kimball in *Mich. Alumnus*
Mar. 1919
*The University of Michigan Museum of Art (bequest
of Henry C. Lewis 1895), Ann Arbor*

162 *GEN. ANTHONY WAYNE (?)*
See no. 60

Miniature 2¾ x 2⅛ / Initialed and dated lower right

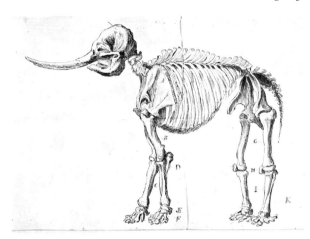

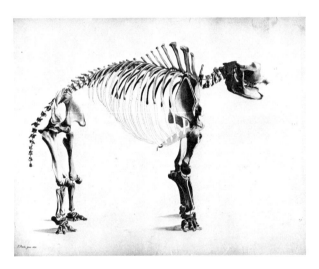

204

1796 / Inscribed on back: Portrait of Major General Anthony Wayne, born January 1, 1745, died December 14, 1796, painted by Rembrandt Peale, 1796 / After Trumbull (?) (Bury) / Sometimes attributed to Raphaelle / Attribution to either brother and identification are open to question; sitter is vaguely reminiscent, in reverse, of James's 1788 "Washington Grays" Washington miniature (Bowen 1892)

Ref.: Bolton 1921 no. 5 / Bury in *Am. Coll.* Aug. 1948

Museum of Art, Carnegie Institute (The Herbert DuPuy Collection 1927), Pittsburgh

OTHER WORKS

163 MASTODON SKELETON

Pen and wash 15¼ x 12¾ / Keyed / Made 1801 for Dr. George Graham who lived near the Masten farm and wrote the first report on the find there of bones of the "great American incognitum" (cf. no. 4, 204)

Ref.: Sellers 1947 / BPM 1956 no. 85

American Philosophical Society Library, Philadelphia

164 HARPERS FERRY

Watercolor 8¼ x 13¼ / 1811 / Signed lower left on mount *R. Peale* / Inscribed below on mount *Harpers Ferry/sketched in* 1812 / Study for no. 165

Exh.: PBM 1825 no. 130 (?) / PAFA 1862 suppl. no. 694 / Peale 1937 no. 21 / —1963 no. 93 / —1965 no. 18 / BPM 1956 no. 75

Ref.: Artist's *sale* 1862 no. 46 / Slatkin 1947

The Trustees of the Municipal Museum of Baltimore

Inc., The Peale Museum (gift of Harry MacNeill Bland)

165 HARPERS FERRY

Canvas 40¼ x 68 / Once attributed to CWP
Coll.: Dr. Conrad Gold, Baltimore (*sale* New York 8 Feb. 1912)
Exh.: Phila. 1811 / PBM / NAD 1826 no. 134 / Peale 1965 no. 18
Ref.: Walker 1913 no. 251 / —1927 no. 225
Walker Art Center, Minneapolis, Minn.

166 THE COURT OF DEATH

Pen and wash 8¼ x 14½ / Study sent in 1819 to *p. 23* CWP, who was helping to finance "The Great Moral Painting" (below)
Exh.: Peale 1937 no. 9 / 1963 no. 60 / BPM 1956 no. 70
Charles Coleman Sellers

167 THE COURT OF DEATH

"In the center a shrouded figure sat upon a shadowy throne, a corpse prostrate at his feet, and around him the attendant throng that accompanies death into the world. The painter's daughters [Rosalba, Angelica, Virginia, Augusta] posed for some of these—Faith, Hope, Virtue, Pleasure. His father—the likeness modified by the bust of Homer —appeared as Old Age. John Neal, his 'friend and critic,' posed as the Warrior, [his brother Franklin as the drunken youth, his infant daughter Emma Clara as the naked orphan] and other friends were represented. The figures fell into three groups, lighted by torchlight, daylight, and reflected light. / Rembrandt's inspiration sprang from a poem, *Death*, by Bielby Porteus, Bishop of London, which was having a tremendous circulation. . . . / In its first thirteen months on tour [it] was viewed by 32 thousand persons and earned more than $9,000." (Sellers 1947) (See no. 150.)

A notice in the Detroit *Democratic Free Press* (2 July 1847) reads in part: "It is the same picture which was exhibited in the Senate Chamber at the Capitol of New York in 1820, and excited so much interest at that time. The artist has, since its first exhibition, almost repainted nearly the whole picture, at an expenditure of more labor than was originally bestowed upon it. It has been exhibited in all the principal eastern cities, and has everywhere elicited the most flattering testimonials of public approbation. It covers 212 square feet, and contains 23 figures of the size of life." A small copy (26 x 36) by Frederick E. Cohen probably was made at this time (Detroit 1962 no. 76)

p. 23 Canvas 138 x 281 / Painted in PBM (BPM) 1820 /
A Sarony, Major & Knapp color lithograph
(15¼ x 26¾), published by G. Q. Colton, New
York 1859, enjoyed great vogue (BPM 1956 no.71)

Exh.: PBM 1820 / Albany 1828 / Utica 1828 (?) /
State Capitol, Detroit 1847 / BPM 1932-44 /
Peale 1937 no. 8 / Detroit 1945 no. 29 / —1957
no. 71

Ref.: Rembrandt in *Nat. Gaz.* (28 Oct. 1820) / —
Crayon Sep. 1857 / Dunlap 1834 / Tuckerman
1867 / Benjamin 1880 / Isham 1905 / *Bull.* July
1910 / —Apr. 1944 / Mather 1927 / Lafollette
1929 / *Art Qu.* Aut. 1945 / Sellers 1947 / —in
Antiques May 1954 / Larkin 1949 / Barker 1950 /
Flexner 1954 / Richardson 1956

*The Detroit Institute of Arts (gift of George H. Scripps
1885)*

168 NIAGARA FALLS

View from the American side

Canvas 18 x 24 / 1832 / Another view was shown in
the Niagara Falls exh. (Buffalo 1964 no. 43)

Exh.: Schenectady 1960 / Buffalo 1960 / —1964
no. 44

Ref.: Artist's *sale* PAFA 1862 no. 50 / New London
1960

*Lyman Allyn Museum (gift of Allan Gerdau 1956),
New London, Conn.*

RUBENS PEALE

(*1784 Philadelphia 1865*)

was the fourth son of C. W. Peale. Because of poor eyesight, he was trained as a naturalist and to be the museum administrator of the family. He was successively manager of the Philadelphia museum (1810-22), of Rembrandt's Baltimore museum (1822-25), and of his own museum in New York (1825-37). In the financial panic of 1837 he sold out to P. T. Barnum and retired to Schuylkill Haven, Pa., where he took up painting, doing still lifes, birds and animals, and landscapes in a primitive vein, frequently copying works by his relatives as well as by others, and receiving painting lessons from them.

STILL LIFES

223

Ref.: Karolik 1949 no. 200 / Sellers in *Art Qu.* Sum. 1960

Museum of Fine Arts, Boston (M. and M. Karolik Collection 1948)

169   STILL LIFE: BASKET OF FRUIT

Canvas 14 x 22 / Signed lower right *Rubens Peale* / His list no. 49: Basket of apples with grapes. Com. Oct. 22, 1860
Coll.: Anna Sellers
Exh.: Greensburg 1959 no. 98

170   STILL LIFE WITH FRUIT

Canvas 19¾ x 26½ / Inscribed on back: Original painted by Rubens Peale, Riverside, 1858—given to M. J. Peale in his 74th year. / Artist's list no. 40: Fruit Piece. China Basket of Peaches, Black Grapes, Cittern Mellon, Cantilope, Cutaba Grapes &c. Com. Aug. 3, 1858. Fin. Nov. 3, 1858. Pres. to Rubens Patterson on Christmass day.
Coll.: M. Karolik
Exh.: Greensburg 1959 no. 97
Ref.: Sellers in *Art Qu.* Sum. 1960

Addison Gallery of American Art, Phillips Academy, Andover, Mass.

171 STILL LIFE: FRUIT ON PEWTER PLATE

p. 38   Tin 13¼ x 19¼ / Rubens Peale list no. 57 (24 Jan. 1861): Commenced a plate of apples for my son Charles representing many of the apples that he brought me to paint from.

Coll.: Coleman Sellers Mills

Exh.: Peale 1960 no. 79

Ref.: Sellers in *Art Qu.* Sum. 1960

Milwaukee Art Center, Layton Art Gallery Collection 1960

172 STILL LIFE: FRUIT PIECE

Canvas 19 x 27 / Inscribed on back: Rubens Peale/ Riverside/1858 / Label on stretcher (fragment): . . . by Rubens Peale / . . . Belonging to Mr. Tatham/...M J Peale / In MS at APS "List of Pictures painted by Rubens Peale at Riverside farm" no. 31, 32, 35 (1857) and 36 (1858) are copies of James Peale *Fruit Piece* belonging to G. N. Tatham.

Coll.: Edward Burd Peale (son) ? / R. Schwartz, Niskayuna, N. Y. / Harvey Handelman, Schenectady, N. Y.

Ref.: Sellers in *Art Qu.* Sum. 1960

Munson-Williams-Proctor Institute, Utica, N. Y.

Apples, &c. by C. W. Peale *(detail of no. 11)* (courtesy MHS)

(detail of no. 107)

(detail of no. 132)

	JAMES PEALE	RAPHAELLE PEALE
Approx. number of located still lifes and estimated total production	35 of 100	35 of 125

Signatures and inscriptions on front	2 at lower left	31—most at lower right
		  14—year only
		    5—year and month
		    7—year, mo. and day
		    5—signed only

Signatures and inscriptions on back	15—usual inscr.: artist's name, age, and date	2
Number per year (dated or datable)	1—1821 / 1—1822 / 1—1824 / 1—1825 / 4—1827 / 2—1828 / 2—1829 / 1—1830	1—1802 / 2—1813 / 4—1815 / 3—1816 / 4—1818 / 5—1821 / 5—1822 / 1—1823
Oil on canvas and average size	25—20 x 26 in.	5—20 x 25 in.
Oil on wood and average size	10—16 x 22 in.	29—12 x 19 in.
Other media and (average) size		Pencil and ink on paper 1—16 x 10¾ in. (1802)
Known or probable replicas and copies	5 replicas	1 replica
Remarks		1 signed: R. Peale 30 give entire (or shortened) first name and last name 2 not signed

(detail of no. 172)

(detail of no. 196)

(detail of no. 217)

RUBENS PEALE	MARGARETTA PEALE	SARAH PEALE
25 of 95	10 of 50	14 of 50
2 (1 also on back)	3 lower right (late 1820s) 2 lower left 1864 and 1865	2 lower right (dated) 3 lower left (dated)
10 (1 also on front)—usual inscr.: artist's name, age, and date	2 (one dated 1829)	2 (one signed, other inscr.: Miss S. M. Peale No. 1015 Spruce Street)
4—1856 / 7—1857 / 2—1858 / 1—1859 / 3—1860 / 1—1861 / 1—1862 / 2—1863 / 2—1864 / 2—1865	4—late 1820s / 1—1864 / 1—1865	3—1820s / 1—1822 / 1—1825 / 1—1828
20—19 x 27 in.	1820s—16 x 21 in. 1860s— 9 x 12 in.	10—14 x 19 in.
	Catalog Deception signed on back	3—13 x 19 in.
oil on tin 5—14 x 20 in.		
32 copies (as indicated by artist's own hand: 14 after James / 9 after Mary Jane / 6 after Raphaelle / 1 after Maria / 2 after unknown) 3 replicas	*Catalog Deception* (after Raphaelle?)	2 after James (?)
	Final digit of some dates illegible	Usual inscr.: Sarah M. Peale. Final digit of some dates illegible

173 THE OLD MUSEUM

p. 21 Tin 14 x 20 / Adapted with much added detail from no. 100 / Artist's list no. 38: View of the back of the house that I was born in. The sketch was made by my Uncle James P. Com. Mar. 6, 1858. Fin. Dec. 22, 1860.
Exh.: Peale 1954 no. 83 / —1963 no. 32 / BPM 1956 no. 97
Ref.: Sellers 1939 / —in *Art Qu.* Sum. 1960
Charles Coleman Sellers

174 PARTRIDGE PIECE: HAPPY FAMILY

Canvas 19½ x 26 / Inscribed on back: Painted by Rubens Peale, Aged 80 years, June 3, 1864 / No. 100 in MS list of artist's work at APS: Partridge Piece, the same as 96 and 97 with a variation of the front ground and positions of the young ones. Commenced March 3, 1864. Finished June 3, 1864. / Cf. same list no. 96: Partridge Piece. The background is a view on the Juniatta from Weber./ —no. 97: Another Happy Family, the same background as 96. / No. 93, 104 and 106 in this list are also partridge pieces or happy families. / For one of these variants see Peale 1960 no. 80.
Ref.: Sellers in *Art Qu.* Sum. 1960
William J. Poplack

175 RUFFED GROUSE IN UNDERBRUSH

Canvas 19¼ x 27¼ / Inscribed on back (before

lining): Painted by Rubens Peale in his eightieth year, April 1864/Artist's list no. 101: Male & Female Pheasant—Commenced Mar. 18, 1864. Finished April 8, 1864. Joseph Patterson. 60.00. / Cf. same list no. 99: Male and Female Pheasant or Ruffed Grouse / Rubens' daughter Mary Jane and his brother Titian also favored this subject (cf. Peale 1960 no. 93-94 and Poesch 1961).

Exh.: Hartford 1942—25 no. 2 / Detroit 1945 no. 39 / Peale 1954 no. 81 / Wilmington 1962 no. 77 / Tucson 1964 no. 149

Ref.: *Bull.* Apr. 1944 / Born 1947 / Jensen 1955 / Richardson 1956 / Pierson 1960 / Sellers in *Art Qu.* Sum. 1960

The Detroit Institute of Arts (gift of Dexter M. Ferry Jr. 1943)

176 STILL LIFE: ORANGE, WINEGLASS AND PANSIES

Canvas 14 x 20¼
Coll.: Lawrence A. Fleischman, Detroit
Exh.: Fleischman 1960 / Newark 1965
Kennedy Galleries Inc.

MARIA PEALE

(*1787 Philadelphia 1866*)

was the second daughter and a pupil of James Peale. She died unmarried.

JAMES PEALE JR.

(*1789 Philadelphia 1876*)

was the only son of James Peale and followed a banking career. In 1822 he married Sophonisba, daughter of his cousin Raphaelle. Two of his sons were also amateur painters, and his daughter Mary Virginia married Augustin Runyon Peale, son of his cousin Linnaeus Peale (no. 13).

"There is an interesting story about James Peale Jr., the watercolorist. As cashier of the Bank of the United States, he signed all the banknotes (as the Treasurer of the U.S. does today). A big gang of counterfeiters in western New York State was issuing fake notes in 1825. He took a leave of absence, joined the gang posing as a crook who could forge J. Peale's name better than they could, and spent ten months with them, preparing an eventual complete round-up of the gang. He returned to Philadelphia as quite a hero." (Letter from James O. Peale, Oct. 1966)

177   SULLY'S STUDIO

Thomas Sully (1783-1872), the most fashionable portrait painter of his time in Philadelphia, was an intimate friend of many of the Peales.

Watercolor 5⅝ x 7⅜ / Signed lower left *J Peale Jr* / Inscribed and dated lower right *Sully's Studio / Octr. 27 '48*

The Detroit Institute of Arts (gift of Robert H. Tannahill 1946)

178   RIVER SCENE

Watercolor 8⅞ x 11⅝ / Signed and dated lower left *Jas. Peale/*1853
Exh.: Peale 1939 no. 12 / BPM 1941 no. 19
Ref.: Karolik 1962 no. 609
Museum of Fine Arts, Boston (M. and M. Karolik Collection 1959)

179   MARINE WITH SHIPPING

Watercolor 8½ x 14½ / Signed and dated lower left *J. Peale Junr/*1859
Exh.: PAFA 1860 no. 373/376 (?) / Peale 1939 no. 10 / —1944 no. 33 / —1954 no. 104 / BPM 1941 no. 18
The Parrish Art Museum (gift of Albert Corning Clark 1958), Southampton, N. Y.

180   THE YACHT AMERICA

A view on the Delaware River below Philadelphia. The boat belonged to the artist's son James Godman Peale (1823-91), also an amateur artist.

Watercolor 8¼ x 14 / Signed and dated lower left *J. Peale/*1863
Exh.: PAFA 1863 no. 452/477 (?)
Ref.: Artist's widow's *sale* 1878 no. 24
James Ogelsby Peale

ANNA CLAYPOOLE PEALE

(*1791 Philadelphia 1878*)

was a daughter and pupil of James Peale. She married Dr. William Staughton (1829), who died within the year, and then Gen. William Duncan (1841). Chiefly a miniaturist, she worked mostly in her native city, but also in New York, Boston, Baltimore and Washington. Anna, as well as her sister Sarah, probably used a studio in her cousin Rembrandt's Baltimore museum and took lessons from him.

Family Portraits

181 *SELF-PORTRAIT*

p. 33 Miniature 2¹⁵⁄₁₆ x 2¼ / Signed and dated lower left
Anna C / Peale / 1818
Coll.: Alexander F. Stevenson
The Art Institute of Chicago (The Colonel Alexander F. and Jeannie C. Stevenson Memorial Collection, gift of Mary Louise Stevenson 1955)

182 *SELF-PORTRAIT*

Canvas 30 x 24 / Perhaps done with the assistance of her cousin Rembrandt Peale
Coll.: Robert Clark Laing, Dearborn, Mich. (*sale New York 13 Apr. 1956 no. 213*)
Exh.: Dearborn 1960 no. 760
Arthur Whallon

183 *JAMES PEALE*
The artist's father (1749-1831)

p. 73 Miniature 1⅜ x 1⅛ / 1820/23 / Inscribed on back: James Peale, Aged 74, painted by Mrs. Staughton (nee Anna C. Peale) when Miss Peale in 1823 / Framed back-to-back with no. 184
Exh.: PAFA 1821 no. 119 (?)
The R. W. Norton Art Gallery, Shreveport

184 *MRS. JAMES PEALE*
Mary Claypoole (1753-1829), the artist's mother

Miniature 1⅜ x 1⅛ / 1820/24 / Inscribed on back: *p. 73*
Mrs. James Peale, aged 70, painted by Mrs. Staughton (nee Anna C. Peale) when Miss Peale, about 1824. / See no. 183
The R. W. Norton Art Gallery, Shreveport

185 *REMBRANDT PEALE*
The artist's first cousin (1778-1860)

Miniature 2⅞ x 2¼ (rect.) / Signed and dated lower *p. 34*
left *Anna C. / Peale* / 1823
Coll.: Francis P. Garvan
The R. W. Norton Art Gallery, Shreveport

ANNA C. PEALE

186 ROSALBA PEALE

The artist's first cousin once removed, Rembrandt's oldest daughter (1799-1874)

p. 34   Miniature 3⅛ x 2¾ (rect.) / Signed and dated lower right *Anna C. Peale* 1820 / See no. 7

The Detroit Institute of Arts (Gibbs-Williams Fund 1953)

187 DR. JAMES STAUGHTON

The artist's stepson

Watercolor 3 x 2⅜ / c. 1830
Exh.: Peale 1963 no. 83
Charles Coleman Sellers

OTHER MINIATURES

188 MARIANNE BECKETT

Later Lady Whichcote

Miniature 3 x 2½ (rect.) / Signed and dated lower right *Anna C. Peale* 1829
Exh.: Greensburg 1959 no. 86
Ref.: HSP 1942

The Historical Society of Pennsylvania (gift of Lena Cadwalader Evans 1939), Philadelphia

189 MRS. ROGER BOYCE

Hannah Maria Day (1780-1854) of Harford

County, Md.

Miniature 2¾ x 2¼ / Signed and dated lower left
Anna C. / Peale / 1818
Coll.: Ella Mackubin (desc.)
Exh.: Peale 1963 no. 53
*Maryland Historical Society (gift through Eleanor
Mackubin 1956), Baltimore*

190   GEN. ANDREW JACKSON (1767-1845)

Seventh President of the United States (1829-37)

p. 33   Miniature 3 x 2½ / Signed and dated lower right
Anna C./Peale/1819 / Cf. canvas by CWP (Sellers
no. 408) posed for at the same time in Washington
(Sellers 1947). In the same year Jackson sat to
Rembrandt at Baltimore for the city (BPM 1956
no. 76); a different portrayal attributed to Rem-
brandt in Lewis coll. at PAFA (1923 no. 19)
appears to be more closely related to John Wesley
Jarvis (cf. MMA 1965)
Exh.: PAFA 1819 no. 116 / New London 1944 no. 87
Ref.: Bolton 1921 no. 3 / *Bull.* June 1937 / —Feb.
1938 / Yale 1951 / Jensen 1955
*Yale University Art Gallery (The Mabel Brady Garvan
Collection 1936), New Haven, Conn.*

191   NATHANIEL KINSMAN (1798-1847)

Miniature 2⅝ x 2⅛ / Signed and dated lower right
Anna C. / Peale / 1819
Coll.: Francis P. Garvan
Exh.: MMA 1939-40 no. L.38.20.3
The R. W. Norton Art Gallery, Shreveport

192   EDGAR ALLAN POE (1809-49)

Poet, critic, short story writer

Miniature 3¹⁵⁄₁₆ x 2¾ / 1834
Exh.: Phila. 1951 no. 224 / Fink 1964 no. 265
*Walters Art Gallery (A. J. Fink Collection 1963),
Baltimore*

(BENJAMIN) FRANKLIN PEALE

(*1795 Philadelphia 1870*)

was next to the youngest son of C. W. Peale. He was trained as a mechanic and worked at the Philadelphia museum. He resigned as museum manager in 1833 for a job at the U. S. Mint, where he became chief coiner (1839-54).

While at the mint Franklin cut the obverse dies for the Indian Peace Medals of Presidents Polk and Taylor. (Reverse dies were in continuous use and had been cut earlier; above, crossed tomahawk and peace pipe; center, clasped hands; inscribed: Peace/ And/Friendship.) For nearly 300 years such medals were given to Indian chiefs to promote peace and friendship between the Indians and their governments by the French, Spanish, British and (later) Americans. The American series, usually in silver, was issued from 1789 to 1889. From 1801 to 1849 American medals were made in three sizes (Franklin Peale's were 76, 62 and 51 mm.), after which the smallest size was discontinued. Presumably the size of the medal presented was determined by the rank of the recipient chief.

193 MEDAL OF PRESIDENT POLK

Indian Peace Medal / James Knox Polk (1795-1849), 11th President of the U.S. (1845-49)

Bronze 3 (diam. 76 mm.) / Inscribed *James K Polk President of the United States.* 1845
Ref.: Loubat 1878 no. 58 / Belden 1927 no. 38
The Henry Ford Museum, Dearborn, Mich.

194 MEDAL OF PRESIDENT TAYLOR

Indian Peace Medal / Zachary Taylor (1784-1850), 12th President of the U.S. (1849-50)

Silver 2$\frac{7}{16}$ (diam. 62 mm.) / Inscribed *Zachary Taylor President of the United States.* 1849.
Ref.: Loubat 1878 no. 64 / Belden 1927 no. 41
The Henry Ford Museum, Dearborn, Mich.

MARGARETTA ANGELICA PEALE

(*1795 Philadelphia 1882*)

was a daughter and pupil of James Peale. Like two of her sisters, who were also painters, she never married.

195   *CATALOG DECEPTION*

Catalogue of Peale's Museum painted by Margaretta Angelica Peale (inscription on back now virtually illegible)

Panel 13½ x 9½ / Incised on back *M A P* / Copy of *Historical Catalogue of the Paintings in the Philadelphia Museum, Consisting Chiefly of Portraits of Revolutionary Patriots and Other Distinguished Characters,* Phila. 1813 / Cf. Raphaelle's *Catalogue for the Use of the Room, a Deception* (PAFA 1812 suppl. no. 201)

James Ogelsby Peale

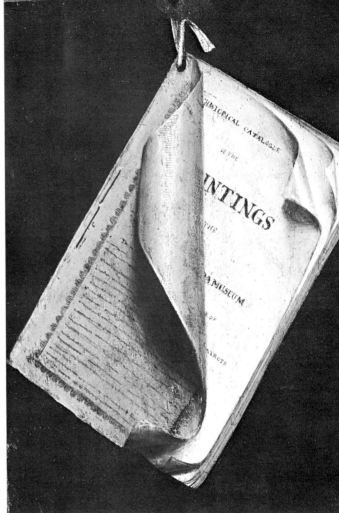

196   *STILL LIFE: GRAPES AND POMEGRANATES*

Canvas 16¼ x 21⅛ / Signed and dated lower right *M. A. Peale* 182-(?)

Coll.: J. Appleton Wilson

Exh.: BPM 1941 no. 21 / Baltimore 1945 no. 38 / Peale 1963 no. 33

Maryland Historical Society (gift of Virginia Appleton Wilson 1958), Baltimore

197   *STILL LIFE: STRAWBERRIES AND CHERRIES*

Canvas 10 x 12¼

Coll.: Mildred Carter, Phila.
Exh.: Peale 1954 no. 107 / Allentown 1959 no. 76
Ref.: Born 1947
The Pennsylvania Academy of the Fine Arts, Philadelphia

ROSALBA CARRIERA PEALE

(*1799 Philadelphia 1874*)

was the eldest daughter of Rembrant Peale and his pupil. She was named for an aunt who died in infancy (and who had been named for an Italian pastelist), and married John A. Underwood rather late in life (1860).

For William Dunlap's *History of the Rise and Progress of the Arts of Design in the United States (New York 1834 v. 2)*, Rembrandt furnished the following note concerning lithography:

"I was among the first of the artists who employed this admirable method of multiplying original drawings. My first attempt in New York was a head of Lord Byron, and a female head from a work of Titian. In 1826 I went to Boston and devoted myself for some time to lithographic studies, and executed a number of portraits and other subjects, and finally a large drawing from my portrait of Washington, for which I obtained the silver medal from the Franklin Institute at Philadelphia in 1827. Unfortunately the workmen, by some neglect, destroyed this drawing on the stone when but a few impressions were taken.

"I instructed one of my daughters and my son in the art, and they produced some very commendable specimens."

198   LANDSCAPE

Lithograph 6½ x 8⅞ (print) / Inscribed below *Drawn on Stone by Rosalba Peale, Boston.*
The Newark Museum (gift of Carol Wirgman 1949)

199   LOCH-LEVEN

Lithograph 6⅜ x 8⅞ (print) / Inscribed below *Miss* *p. 20* *Rosalba Peale, Lith: Loch-Leven*
The Newark Museum (gift of Carol Wirgman 1949)

200   ROBERT MORRIS (*1734-1806*)

Financier / Robert Edge Pine (1730-88) was his artist protege. / Morris was also portrayed by CWP

(Sellers no. 573-79) and Rembrandt.

Board 8¾ x 7 / Inscribed on back: Robert Morris/
copy of portrait by/Rembrandt Peale/painted by
(a?) Miss Peale/and given to/(Miss?) Elisth White
/ Same pose as engraving in Longacre and
Herring's NPG (v. 4, 1846) with legend: Engraved
by T. B. Welch from a Painting by J. B. Longacre
after an original Portrait by R. E. Pine

*The Dayton Art Institute (gift of John McIntyre
1959), Dayton, Ohio*

TITIAN RAMSAY PEALE

(*1799 Philadelphia 1885*)

was the youngest son of C. W. Peale, named for his
half-brother (1780-98). Titian II, the naturalist and
scientific illustrator of the family, went on several
expeditions: Florida and Georgia (1817-18), Long's
expedition to the upper Missouri River (1819-20),
Florida again (1824), and Wilkes's expedition to the
South Seas (1838-42). Meantime he worked at the

Philadelphia museum and became manager (1833).
After the expedition to the South Seas, Titian settled
in Washington and worked at the U. S. Patent Office
(1848-73). His later years were spent in Philadelphia.
(See also biography of Coleman Sellers.)

201   SELF-PORTRAIT

Canvas 24 x 20 / c. 1850 / Inscribed on back: T. R.
Peale—by himself with a little help from his
brother Rembrandt. Mrs. T. R. Peale to John
Hoffmire, Red Bank, 1886

Coll.: John Hoffmire, Red Bank, N. J. (nephew)
Exh.: Peale 1960 no. 83
Ref.: Poesch 1961
The American Museum of Natural History, New York

NATURE STUDIES

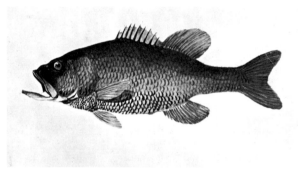

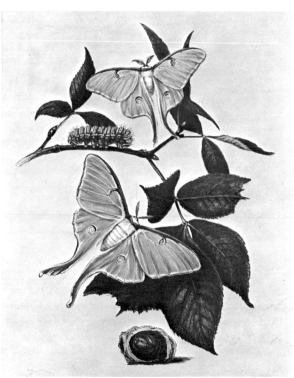

202 FISH

Pencil and watercolor 5½ x 8½ / Inscribed below
No. 1/New Orleans 31st Nov. 1820
Ref.: *Bull.* Dec. 1957
American Philosophical Society Library, Philadelphia

203 GREEN MOTHS

Watercolor 12 x 10 / Signed and dated lower right
T R Peale 1876
Exh.: Detroit 1962 no. 25
Mr. and Mrs. Harold O. Love

204 MASTODON SKELETON

Pen and wash 14½ x 19 / Inscribed lower left   *p. 113*
T Peale Jan. 1821 / Cf. no. 4, 163
American Philosophical Society Library, Philadelphia

205 THREE SHOREBIRDS

Watercolor 10¼ x 14¼ / Inscribed below *By T. R.
Peale*
Exh.: Peale 1963 no. 114
American Philosophical Society Library, Philadelphia

206 WHITE BEAR

Pencil and watercolor 5½ x 9¼ / Inscribed below
*male/Philadela. Jan 3d 1830 Doolittle & Cos.
managerie. 5 years old?*
Ref.: *Bull.* Dec. 1957
American Philosophical Society Library, Philadelphia

OTHER WORKS

207 INDIAN BRAVE ON HORSEBACK

Pencil and watercolor 5½ x 9¼ / 1819/20 / No.
upper right: 40 / Verso: pencil sketches of Indians
and horses used for 1873 painting "Buffalo Kill"
(Poesch)
Ref.: Poesch 1961 / Ewers 1965
American Philosophical Society Library, Philadelphia

**208 TWO INDIAN BRAVES HUNTING
BUFFALO**

Pencil 5½ x 8½ / 1819/20 / No. upper right: 41 /
Horseman to right derived from sketch 40 (above)
/ Cf. "Buffaloe Hunt on the River Platte. Painted
by T. R. Peale. P. S. Duval Lithr. Phila." in
J. O. Lewis' *Aboriginal Portfolio* c. 1836, and 1873
painting of same subject (both in Poesch 1961).

Ref.: *Bull.* Dec. 1957
American Philosophical Society Library, Philadelphia

209 INTERIOR OF PEALE'S MUSEUM

Watercolor 14 x 20¾ / Inscribed on back: Interior
of front room/Peale's Museum/State House/
Philadelphia/1822/by T. R. Peale / Study begun
by CWP for background of no. 2
Ref.: R. C. Smith in *Art Qu.* Aut. 1958 / J. Poesch
in *Antiques* Oct. 1960

The Detroit Institute of Arts (gift of the Founders Society Director's Fund 1957)

210 INTERIOR OF KILAUEA, HAWAII

One of the largest active volcanic craters in the world

Canvas 17 x 20 / Signed and dated lower right *T. R. Peale*/1840
Coll.: John Hoffmire, Red Bank, N.J. (nephew)
Exh.: Peale 1960 no. 85
Ref.: Poesch 1961

The American Museum of Natural History, New York

211 BRIGHT HOUSE

Board 8½ x 12 / Signed and dated lower left
Rehoboth/T R Peale/Aug 1882 / Old label on
back: T R Peale 12 Aug 82/Bright House/
Rehoboth Beach Del

Coll.: Lawrence A. Fleischman, Detroit

Exh.: Fleischman 1960 / —1964 no. 79

Ref.: *Antiques* Nov. 1964 / *Kennedy Qu.* Oct. 1966
no. 172

Dr. and Mrs. Irving Levitt

HARRIET CANY PEALE

(*c. 1800—Philadelphia 1869*)

was a pupil and the second wife of Rembrandt
(m. 1840). Most of her known works seem to be
copies after those of other artists.

212 *IDEAL PORTRAIT*

Also called Odalisque and Female Figure with
Turban

Canvas 25 x 30 / Signed lower right *H. C. Peale* /
Apparently after a work by her husband dated
1845 (Pittsburgh 1925 no. 24)

Exh.: Greensburg 1959 no. 88

Ref.: *Bull.* Aug. 1964

*Norfolk Museum of Arts and Sciences (gift of Edward
J. Brickhouse 1964)*

213 *LANDSCAPE*

Board 9½ x 12½ / Inscribed on back: Landscape by
Mrs. Rembrandt Peale, Phila.—1858

Exh.: Newark 1965

The Newark Museum (gift of Carol Wirgman 1949)

SARAH MIRIAM PEALE

(*1800 Philadelphia 1885*)

was the youngest daughter and a pupil of James
Peale. Early she worked chiefly in Philadelphia and
Baltimore, and accompanied her uncle C. W. Peale
and her sister Anna to Washington in 1818. Sarah
lived in Baltimore and had her studio in the Peale
Museum there from about 1820 to 1829, where she
undoubtedly received painting lessons from her
cousin Rembrandt. Lafayette sat to her four times
in 1825. In 1847 she went to St. Louis, returning to
Philadelphia in 1875.

Sarah Miriam Peale is sometimes acclaimed as the
first professional woman artist in the United States.

214 SELF-PORTRAIT

Canvas 24 x 19 / 1818 / Traditionally her first oil portrait, assisted by her father, who used same pose in his later portrait of her (Peale 1923 no. 202)
Exh.: PAFA 1818 no. 43 / Peale 1954 no. 110 / — 1963 no. 35 / —1965 no. 31 / BPM 1956 no. 99
Ref.: Jensen 1955
Charles Coleman Sellers

215 MRS. RUBENS PEALE AND SON

Eliza Burd Patterson (1795-1864) and Charles Willson Peale (1821-71)

Canvas 30 x 24 / 1823 / Inscribed on back (before lining): Mrs. Rubens Peale and her son Charles, Painted by Sarah Peale in Baltimore c. 1822
Coll.: Helen Elizabeth Mills Weisenberg (desc.) / Coleman Sellers Mills

Exh.: Peale 1963 no. 34 / —1965 on. 32
Ref. BPM 1964
The Trustees of the Municipal Museum of Baltimore Inc., The Peale Museum

216 ANNA MARIA SMYTH
Later Mrs. Matthew J. Bernside

Canvas 36 x 28 / Signed and dated lower right
Sarah M. Peale/1821
Exh.: Lewis 1934 no. 140 / Peale 1963 no. 38
The Pennsylvania Academy of the Fine Arts (John Frederick Lewis Collection), Philadelphia

217 STILL LIFE: GRAPES AND WATERMELON

Canvas 14¼ x 19 / Signed and dated lower left
Sarah M. Peale 1828

217

216

Coll.: J. Appleton Wilson
Exh.: PAFA 1829 no. 33 (?) / BPM 1941 no. 23 /
    Baltimore 1945 no. 41 / Peale 1963 no. 36
Maryland Historical Society (gift of Virginia Apple-
ton Wilson 1958), Baltimore

MARY JANE SIMES

(1807 Baltimore 1872)

was the daughter of Jane Ramsay Peale Simes,
eldest daughter of James Peale. She married Dr.
John Floyd Yeates and had four children. Noting
that Anna Peale was well known as a miniature
painter, William Dunlap remarked that her "niece,
Mary Jane Simes, herself a living miniature, rivals
her aunt in the same style." (1834)

218 MRS. ROBERT HARDIE
    Emily Jane McClure (1808-91) / Pendant of Capt.
Hardie (1798-1881) also at MHS.

Miniature 2⅞ x 2 / Inscribed on back: Painted by/   *p. 34*
    Miss M. J. Simes/Baltimore/1832
Ref.: MHS 1945
Maryland Historical Society (gift of her daughter
Ella Howard Hardie 1924), Baltimore

WASHINGTON PEALE

(1825 Philadelphia—
San Juan, Puerto Rico 1868)

was the second son of James Peale Jr. Known as a landscapist and commercial artist, Washington Peale's short life indicates, perhaps, that he followed in the tradition of his brilliant cousin Raphaelle.

(MICHAEL) ANGELO PEALE

(1814 Baltimore—Philadelphia 1833)

was Rembrandt's younger son. He seems to be the last Peale named directly for an artist rather than for a relative who was named for an artist. At that, he was known as Angelo instead of Mike. His father was making arrangements for him to study art in England when he died. Angelo's twin sister Emma Clara, the youngest of eight daughters, was also an artist. She is said to have designed the label for a cologne.

It is, perhaps, more appropriate than peculiar that Rembrandt taught the new art of lithography only to those of his ten children who bore the full names of famous artists—Rosalba (see above) and her brother Angelo.

219   A CHURCH

Lithograph 9½ x 6½ / Signed below *A. Peale del.* /
  Autograph inscription *Angelo Peale/Second attempt*
Charles Coleman Sellers

220   ITALIAN ARCH AND TOWER

Lithograph 9½ x 6½ / Signed below *Angelo Peale Del.*
Exh.: Peale 1963 no. 80
Charles Coleman Sellers

221   SELF-PORTRAIT

Board 7⅝ (diam.)
James Ogelsby Peale

222   MUSIC COVER

Columbia Mourns Her Citizens Slain

Lithograph 10¾ x 8½ (paper 14 x 10¾) / 1844 /
  Inscribed lower left *On Stone by Wash Peale* /
  Published by Colon & Adriance, Phildelphia
Library of Congress, Washington, D.C.

223 RUBENS PEALE

The artist's father (1784-1865)/She also portrayed her mother (Peale 1960 no. 91)

Canvas 30 x 25 / Inscribed on back: Rubens Peale, painted by Mary J. Peale, Woodland, April 1855, aged 71 *p. 116*
Coll.: Coleman Sellers Mills
Exh.: Peale 1960 no. 92
Kennedy Galleries Inc.

224 THE PEARL OF GRIEF

Canvas 24 x 18 / Inscribed on back: Rem Peale's Pearl of Grief / Copied by / M J Peale / 1855 / Original was shown at PAFA 1862 (suppl. no. 714).
Robert Carlen

225 STILL LIFE WITH BOWL OF FRUIT

Bowl is monogrammed R P

Canvas 19 x 27½ / Inscribed and dated on back: Original/by/Mary J. Peale/Riverside/1860/The large dark grapes/received the prize at the Agricultural fair in/Reading
Exh.: Greensburg 1959 no. 94
Ref.: Flexner 1962
William J. Poplack

MARY JANE PEALE

(1827 New York, N. Y.— Pottsville, Pa. 1902)

was the only daughter of Rubens Peale (she had six brothers). A pupil of her uncle Rembrandt and of Thomas Sully, she in turn instructed her father. She died unmarried.

COLEMAN SELLERS

(1827 Philadelphia 1907)

was the youngest son of Sophonisba Angusciola, daughter of CWP. Although a professional engineer, Coleman and his uncle Titian were serious amateurs of the new art of photography and carried on a lively correspondence about it between Philadelphia and Washington. Titian processed his invention of the Kinematoscope through the Patent Office for him (1861). (He took out a number of other patents, notably the Sellers coupling.) In the same year,

together with Oliver Wendell Holmes and others, they founded the first photographic club in the U.S. —the Amateur Photographic Exchange Club. Later Sellers participated in the development of hydro-electric power at Niagara Falls, becoming president of the Niagara Falls Power Co.

His older brother George Escol Sellers (1808-99), an inventor and manufacturer, was also an amateur artist (Peale 1963 no. 123).

226 *REMBRANDT AND HARRIET PEALE*

His uncle and his second wife with one of their "standard" (36 x 29) portholes of Washington (see no. 159)

Photograph / c. 1859   *p. 100*
Ref.: Taft 1938

Courtesy The Peale Museum, Baltimore

ABBREVIATED GENEALOGY

Charles Peale Jr. (1709-50) was the father of no. 1—5, Charles Willson (1) was the father of no. 1.3—1.17 (some children who died in infancy, such as no. 1.1—1.2, are omitted), Elizabeth (4) was the mother of no. 4.2, etc. Thus under James (5) we find that his son James (5.3) married Sophonisba (1.5.3), the daughter of Charles Willson's son Raphaelle (1.5). This abbreviated genealogy (the first and second American-born generations are fairly complete; the third, not at all) was based on the extensive family records in *Charles Willson Peale: Later Life* by Charles Coleman Sellers (Phila. 1947), pp. 412-23, where the identity of some persons not listed here (hence our missing numbers) may be found.

Known artists are indicated by an asterisk (*).

Charles Peale Jr. (1709-50) m. 1740 Margaret Triggs Matthews (1709-91)

*1 Charles Willson Peale (1741-1827) m. (1) 1762 Rachel Brewer (1744-90)

    1.3 Eleanor Peale (1770—d. in infancy)

    1.4 Margaret Van Peale (1772-72/3)

  *1.5 Raphaelle Peale (1774-1825) m. 1797 Martha Ann McGlathery (1775-1852)

        1.5.3 Sophonisba Peale (1801-78) m. 1822 *James Peale Jr. (5.3)

        1.5.4 Charles Willson Peale (1802-29) m. 1828 Hannah Hopkins (b. 1805)

        1.5.7 Rubens Peale (1808-91) m. 1837 Ann Creamer (1810-98)

        1.5.8 Margaret Peale (1810-47) m. 1829 *John Carr (d. 1837)

  *1.6 Angelica Kauffmann Peale (1775-1853) m. 1794 Alexander Robinson (1751-1845)

  *1.7 Rembrandt Peale (1778-1860) m. (1) 1798 Eleanor May Short (1776-1836)

    *1.7.1 Rosalba Carriera Peale (1799-1874) m. 1860 *John A. Underwood

    1.7.2 Angelica Peale (1800-59) m. 1821 Dr. John Davidson Godman (1794-1830)

    1.7.3 Virginia Peale (1803-86)

1.7.4 Augusta Peale *twin* (1805-86) m. 1827 Dr. Charles Otis Barker (d. 1843)

1.7.5 Eleanor Peale *twin* (1805-77) m. 1825 Thomas H. Jacobs

1.7.6 Henrietta Peale (1806-92) m. Dr. John H. Griscom (1809-74)

1.7.7 Henry Peale *twin* (1812-25)

1.7.8 Mary J. Peale *twin* (1812-76)

*1.7.9 Michael Angelo Peale *twin* (1814-33)

*1.7.10 Emma Clara Peale *twin* (1814-82) m. (1) 1838 Rev. James A. Peabody, m. (2) 1845 Caleb D. Barton

*1.7 Rembrandt Peale m. (2) 1840 *Harriet Cany (c. 1800-69)

*1.8 Titian Ramsay Peale I (1780-98)

*1.9 Rubens Peale (1784-1865) m. 1820 Eliza Burd Patterson (1795-1864)

    1.9.1 Charles Willson Peale (1821-71) m. Harriet Friel

    1.9.2 George Patterson Peale (1822-58)

    1.9.3 William Peale (1824-38)

  *1.9.4 Mary Jane Peale (1827-1902)

    1.9.5 James Burd Peale (1833-81) m. (1) 1859 Clarissa McBurney, m. (2) 1868 Mary Rebecca Frisby Wilmer

1.9.6   Rubens Peale *twin* (1836-37)
1.9.7   Edward Burd Peale *twin* (1836-1905) m. 1859 Louisa Harriet Hubley
1.10   Sophonisba Angusciola Peale (1786-1859) m. 1805 Coleman Sellers (1781-1834)
 *1.10.2   George Escol Sellers (1808-99) m. 1833 Rachel Brooks Parrish (1812-60)
 *1.10.6   Coleman Sellers (1827-1907) m. 1851 Cornelia Wells (1832-1909)
1.11   Rosalba Carriera Peale (1788-90)
*1   Charles Willson Peale m. (2) 1791 Elizabeth DePeyster (1765-1804)
1.12   Vandyke Peale (1792)
1.13   (Charles) Linnaeus Peale (1794-1832) m. 1817 Christiana Runyon (d. 1839)
 1.13.2   Augustin Runyon Peale (1819-56) m. 1845 Mary Virginia Peale (5.3.4)
*1.14   (Benjamin) Franklin Peale (1795-1870) m. (1) 1815 Eliza Greatrake, m. (2) 1839 Caroline E. Girard Haslam (d. 1875)
1.15   Sybilla Miriam Peale (1797-1856) m. 1815 Andrew Summers III (1795-1843)
*1.16   Titian Ramsay Peale II (1799-1885) m. (1) 1822 Eliza Cecilia Laforgue (d. 1846), m. (2) 1850 Lucinda MacMullen
1.17   Elizabeth DePeyster Peale (1802-57) m. 1820 William Augustus Patterson (1792-1833)
*1   Charles Willson Peale m. (3) 1805 Hannah Moore (1755-1821)
2   Margaret Jane Peale (1743-88) m. (1) c. 1760 James McMordia (d. c. 1767), m. (2) 1771 Nathaniel Ramsay (1741-1817)

*3   Saint George Peale (1745-78) m. *Elizabeth Emerson Callister (d. c. 1786)
4   Elizabeth Digby Peale (1747-c. 76) m. 1765 Robert Polk (1744-77)
 *4.2   Charles Peale Polk (1767-1822) m. (1) c. 1785 Ruth Ellison, m. (2) c. 1811 Mrs. Brockenbrough, m. (3) c. 1816 Ellen B. Downman
 4.3   Elizabeth Bordley Polk (b. 1770) m. (1) Septimus Claypoole (d. 1798), m. (2) Rev. Dr. Joseph G. J. Bend (d. 1812)
*5   James Peale (1749-1831) m. 1782 Mary Chambers Claypoole (1753-1829)
 5.1   Jane Ramsay Peale (1785-1834) m. 1806 Dr. Samuel Simes (d. 1813)
  *5.1.1   Mary Jane Simes (1807-72) m. 1836 Dr. John Floyd Yeates
 *5.2   Maria Peale (1787-1866)
 *5.3   James Peale (1789-1876) m. 1822 Sophonisba Peale (1.5.3)
  *5.3.1   James Godman Peale (1823-91) m. 1846 Ellen Quillicent Millicent Field
  *5.3.2   Washington Peale (1825-68) m. 1845 Margaret Briggs
  5.3.4   Mary Virginia Peale (1828-67) m. 1845 Augustin Runyon Peale (1.13.2)
 *5.4   Anna Claypoole Peale (1791-1878) m. (1) 1829 Rev. Dr. William Staughton (1770-1829), m. (2) 1841 Gen. William Duncan (1772-1864)
 *5.6   Margaretta Angelica Peale (1795-1882)
 *5.7   Sarah Miriam Peale (1800-85)

125   *(detail)*

ACKNOWLEDGMENTS

The assistance and cooperation of the owners and lenders of the works of art in the exhibition, of the authors of the articles in this book, and of many persons, including the following, associated with various organizations have made this work possible:

Philip R. Adams, Paul A. Amelia, Leon A. Arkus, Vincent R. Artz, Tracy Atkinson, Mildred Baker, Whitfield J. Bell Jr., Katharine Beneker, Francis W. Bilodeau, George O. Bird, C. Dean Blair, Robin Bolton-Smith, William A. Bostick, Edgar Breitenbach, Virginia H. Brose, Ruth E. Brown, Charles E. Buckley, Thomas S. Buechner, Doris Burton, Janet S. Byrne

Henry Cadwalader, Henry B. Caldwell, William B. Campbell, Marion B. Carr, Mary E. Carver, Paul A. Chew, Elizabeth Clare, Mark A. Clark, Katherine Coffey, Thomas C. Colt Jr., James S. Copley, George W. Corner, Perry B. Cott, Frederick Cummings, Charles C. Cunningham, G. Anne Daly, Samuel David, Margaret M. De Grace, Jean Dodenhoff, Phyllis Donaldson, Alan B. Du Bois

Eleanor P. Ediger, J. Kenton Eisenbrey, James Elliott, Marjorie L. Ellis, Frances Ettinge, Bruce H. Evans, Stuart P. Feld, Lawrence A. Fleischman, Henry S. Francis, Joseph T. Fraser Jr., Martin L. Friedman, Henry G. Gardiner, William H. Gerdts, Patricia R. Geyer, Donald M. Glover, Margaret Goodenough, John M. Graham II, Robert C. Graham, Gertrude Grawn, George F. Green, Paul L. Grigaut, Gustave von Groschwitz, Audley M. Grossman Jr., Samuel C. Gundy

Marion J. Hamilton, James Harithas, Bartlett H. Hayes Jr., James J. Heslin, Gertrude D. Hess, Lela M. Hine, Eugenia Calvert Holland, Donelson F. Hoopes, Rosemary B. Hopkins, Hannah J. Howell, Richard H. Howland, Wilbur H. Hunter,

Lawrence Jackson, Stephen B. Jareckie, Oliver Jensen, Milton Kaplan, James O. Keene, Ruth Keene, Winifred Kennedy, Joy Kenseth, Joan Kerr, James R. Ketchum, Joe Kindig Jr., Clara M. King, Jacqueline S. Klein, Joseph Klima Jr., Audrey Koenig, Karl Kup, Rupert Latture, Thomas W. Leavitt, Sherman E. Lee, David B. Little, Doris Lockwood

Helen G. McCormack, Garnett McCoy, Mildred S. McGill, J. Richard McGregor, John J. McKendry, Virginia McMillan, Robert L. McNeil Jr., John A. Mahey, Harold R. Manakee, Jan van der Marck, John Maxon, Edgar deN. Mayhew, David Milgrome, Marie B. Miller, John C. Milley, Dorothy Minett, Helene Monroe, Charles H. Morgan, Sarah E. Morris, Diana M. Muller, Alden Murray, Charles Nagel, Edmund B. Nielsen, Richard W. Norton Jr., James A. Oliver, Muriel O'Neil

A. Franklin Page, Charles Parkhurst, Frank A. Parsons, Wilbur D. Peat, William Peck, George A. Periet, F. Warren Peters, Jean A. Peyrat, Andrew Poggenpohl, Richard H. Randall Jr., Perry T. Rathbone, Emily S. Rauh, Charles van Ravenswaay, James H. Ricau, Daniel C. Rich, Edgar P. Richardson, Andrew C. Ritchie, H. Radclyffe Roberts, Gordon H. Robertson, Francis W. Robinson, Frederick B. Robinson, Robert R. Rodgers, Francis S. Ronalds, Gertrude Rosenthal, E. J. Rousuck, Louise Rowley

Herbert J. Sanborn, Helen Satz, Charles H. Sawyer, Morris Schapiro, Henrietta M. Schumm, Marvin D. Schwartz, Carolyn Scoon, David W. Scott, Carol E. Selby, Ellen Sharp, Harold T. Shaw, Donald A. Shelley, Carolyn R. Shine, Clifford K. Shipton, Laurence Sickman, Walter E. Simmons Jr., Murphy D. Smith, Victor D. Spark, Nina E. Sperandeo, Robert E. Springer,

Mildred Steinbach, Robert G. Stewart, Frederick A. Sweet

Carolyn M. Taylor, Nicki. Thiras, Margaret C. Toole, Evan H. Turner, Valerie Vondermuhll, John Walker, David H. Wallace, Louise Wallman, Allen Wardwell, David B. Warren, Carl J. Weinhardt Jr., Robert T. Weston, Hermann W. Williams Jr., Honor Williams, R. N. Williams II, Dorothy Wing, Otto Wittmann, Ann Woods, William E. Woolfenden, Richard P. Wunder, Rudolf G. Wunderlich

All color plates and photographs are courtesy the owners and lenders. Color plates also courtesy: *Exhuming the Mastodon* (detail of no. 4), American Heritage Publishing Co. Inc. (photograph Wilbur H. Hunter), page 1; *The Artist in his Museum* (detail of no. 2), Time Incorporated, page 2; *Benjamin Franklin* (no. 28), American Philosophical Society and *National Geographic Magazine*, page 6; *Exhuming the Mastodon* (no. 4), The Peale Museum and *National Geographic Magazine*, page 15; *The Staircase Group* (no. 10), The Metropolitan Museum of Art and American Heritage Publishing Co. Inc., page 16; *The Lamplight Portrait* (no. 7), Thomas Y. Crowell Co., page 17; *John Paul Jones* (no. 33), Time Incorporated and American Heritage Publishing Co. Inc., page 22; *Paul Beck Jr.* (no. 81), *Bulletin of the Carnegie Institute*, page 31; *Andrew Jackson* (no. 190), American Heritage Publishing Co. Inc., page 33

Additional photographic credits: Frick Art Reference Library, no. 19, 29, 46, 61, 63, 67, 68, 82, 116, 123, 144, 166, 196, 217, 218; Alice Hook and Cincinnati Art Museum, no. 37, 38; J. William Middendorf II, no. 58; *Life Magazine*, no. 141; The Peale Museum, no. 143, 165, 226; Joseph Klima Jr., no. 55, 65, 107, 110, 111, 139, 180, 195, 198, 199, 203, 221, 224

REFERENCES

References are not exhaustive; most were kindly furnished by lenders and owners, and in some cases selections were made. The resources of the Archives of American Art, the Detroit Public Library, the Frick Art Reference Library (FARL), the New York Public Library, and the Research Library of the Detroit Institute of Arts were used. Biographical literature concerning sitters was scarcely tapped. More complete titles of most of the "key word" citations in this catalog are given below in the bibliography; a few were not located.

ABBREVIATIONS AND DEFINITIONS

For plurals and many derivative and related words, abbreviations usually were not inflected; some familiar ones not listed here were also used.

AFA American Federation of Arts / AM. America(n) / AMNH American Museum of Natural History, New York / APS American Philosophical Society, Phila./ASCR. ascribe(d)/ATTR. attribute(d) / B. born / BOARD: cardboard or similar composition board, other than wood (panel) / BPM Peale Museum (Municipal Mus. of City of Baltimore) / BULL. bulletin (esp. of owner); serial pub. which may have other title, e.g. *Museum News* of Toledo Mus. of Art

CANVAS (can.): cloth fabric supporting oil paint / CAT. catalog (esp. of owner's coll.) / CEN. center /

CENT. century / CF. see also; compare / COLL. collect(or)(s), collection(s) / CWP Charles Willson Peale / D. died / DASH (—): (special use) repeat first (or pertinent) word(s) of preceding entry / DATES: c. means *about, around;* an unspaced virgule (/) means *or,* or any year between those given (virgules spaced on either side separate consecutive entries); a hyphen (-) indicates period of production for works and span of life for persons (dash (—) also used for latter, esp. in captions) / DESC. descendant(s) / DIA Detroit Institute of Arts / DIMENSIONS (e.g. 6 x 5½) are in inches, height first / DRAWINGS (charcoal, crayon, pencil, etc.) are on paper

ENGR. engraving; cf. prints / EXH. exhibit(ed), exhibition(s); cf. ref. / GALL. gallery(-ies) / H. height / HIST. historic(al), history / HSP Historical Society of Pennsylvania, Phila. / INHP Independence National Historical Park, Phila. / INSCR. inscribe(d), inscription(s) / INST. institute(s), institution(s)

M. married / MEM. memorial / MFA Museum of Fine Arts / MHS Maryland Historical Society, Baltimore / MINIATURES (min.) are watercolors on ivory and oval unless qualified (cf. rect.) / MMA Metropolitan Museum of Art, New York / MOMA Museum of Modern Art, New York / MUS. museum(s) / NAD National Academy of Design, New York / NCFA National Coll. of Fine Arts, Washington, D.C. / NGA National Gallery of Art, Washington, D.C. / NGM *Nat. Geographic Mag.* / NO. number(s)

/ NPG National Portrait Gall., Washington, D.C. /
NYHS New-York Historical Society, New York
OWNER (lender): full name is in *italics* at close of
each entry / PAFA Pennsylvania Academy of the
Fine Arts, Phila. / PAL. palace / PANEL: wood
supporting paint / PBM "Peale's Baltimore Museum" / PHILA. Philadelphia, Pa. / PORTR. portrait(s),
portray(ed)(s) / PPM "Peale's Philadelphia
Museum" / PRINTS are on paper; citations under
exh. and *ref.* may be to impressions or states other
than those in this exh. / QU. quarterly

RECT. rectangle, rectilinear / REF. reference(s);
normally citations given under *exh.* are not repeated
/ SELLERS NO.: C. C. Sellers *Portr. and Min. by
CWP* Phila. 1952 (with item no.; second no., if any,
is that of plate) / SIZE: see dimensions / USNM
United States National Mus., Washington, D.C. /
VAR. variant(s) / WAC Walker Art Center, Min-
neapolis, Minn. / WAG Walters Art Gallery, Balti-
more / WATERCOLORS are on paper / YUAG Yale
Univ. Art Gall., New Haven, Conn.

BIBLIOGRAPHY

AFA 1953: *19th Cent. Am. Painting* traveling exh. in Germany
(Frankfort, Munich, Hamburg, Berlin, Dusseldorf) and Italy
1954 (Trieste, Rome)
—1965: *Watercolors and Drawings from Karolik Coll.* circ. exh.
Allentown 1959: *4 Cent. of Still Life* Art Mus.
Amherst 1950: *"Benj. West"* Art in Am. Dec.
Argosy 1953: *Am. Art* New York, Gall.
Asheville 1949: *Am. Portr.* (N.C.) Pack Mem. Pub. Lib.
Atlanta 1951: *Am. Portr. from NGA* High Mus. of Art
Baker 1880: W. Baker *Engr. Portr. of Washington* Boston
Baltimore 1938: *200 Years of Am. Painting* Mus. of Art
—1945: *250 Years of Painting in Md.*
—1956: *Cat. of Am. Works of Art* WAG
—1958: *J. Hall Pleasants Mem. Exh.* Mus. of Art
Barker 1950: V. Barker *Am. Painting* New York
Baur 1940: J. Baur "Peales and Development of Am. Still Life"
Art Qu. Winter
Belden 1927: B. Belden *Indian Peace Medals* New York
Benjamin 1880: S. Benjamin *Art in Am.* New York

Bolton 1921: T. Bolton *Early Am. Portr. Painters in Min.* N.Y.
—1923: *Early Am. Portr. Draughtsmen in Crayons* New York
—1939: "CWP" *Art Qu.* Aut. suppl.
Born 1947: W. Born *Still Life Painting in Am.* New York
Boston 1921: *Cat. of Paintings* MFA
Bowen 1892: C. Bowen *Hist. of Centennial Celebration of Inaugu-
ration of Geo. Washington as Pres. of U.S.* New York
BPM 1941: "Paintings and Watercolors by Peales" *Bull.* 15 Dec.
—1956: *Rendezvous for Taste*
—1964: *Story of Am. Oldest Mus. Bldg.*
Briggs 1952: B. Briggs *CWP: Artist & Patriot* New York
Brockway 1932: J. Brockway "Min. of James Peale" *Antiques* Oct.
Brooklyn 1917: *Early Am. Paintings* Inst. of Arts and Sc.
—1936: *5 Cent. of Min. Painting* Mus.
—1944: *Am. 1744-1944*
—1953: *Am. Painting in Mus. Coll.*
—1957: *Face of Am.*
Buffalo 1964: *3 Cent. of Niagara Falls* Albright-Knox Art Gall.
Burroughs 1936: A. Burroughs *Limners and Likenesses* Cambridge
Bury 1948: E. Bury "Raphaelle Peale Min. Painter" *Am. Coll.*
Aug.
Caffin 1907: C. Caffin *Story of Am. Painting* New York
Cahill 1935: H. Cahill and A. Barr *Art in Am.* New York
Carrick 1928: A. Carrick *Shades of Our Ancestors* Boston
Century 1926: *Early Am. Painting* New York, Assoc.
Charlotte 1952: *Am. Exh.* (N.C.) Mint Mus.
Chattanooga 1952: *Inaugural Exh.* Hunter Gall. of Art
Chicago 1949: *From Colony to Nation* Art Inst.
—1961: *Paintings* (cat.)
Cincinnati 1852: *Cat. of Nat. Portr. & Hist. Gall.* Independence
Hall
—1958: *2 Cent. of Am. Painting* Art Mus.
Clarke 1919: *Early Am. Portr. Coll. by Thos. B. Clarke* New York,
Plaza Hotel (*sale*) 7 Jan.
—1928: *Portr. by Early Am. Artists Coll. by Thos. B. Clarke* Phila.
Mus. of Art
Cleveland 1936: *20th Anniv. Exh.* Mus. of Art
Colorado Springs 1949: *Likeness of Am. 1680-1820* Fine Arts Cen.
Columbia 1950: *Face of Am. Hist.* (S.C.) Mus. of Art
Columbus 1947: *Colonial Am.* (Ohio) Gall. of Fine Arts
—1958: *Reynolds and Am. Contemporaries*
Comstock 1950: H. Comstock *Am. Lithographs of 19th Cent.*
New York
Cook 1888: C. Cook *Art and Artists of Our Time* New York
Dallas 1960: *Famous Families in Am. Art* MFA
Dearborn 1960: *Americana: Midwest Coll. Choice* Henry Ford Mus.
Denver 1948: *Am. Heritage* Art Mus.
—1952: *Man at Work*
—1958: *Great Ideas of Western Man*
Des Moines 1953: *Realism in Painting & Sculpture* Art Cen.

Detroit 1945: *World of Romantic Artist* DIA
—B: *Am. Birds and their Painters and Sculptors*
—1944: *Cat. of Paintings*
—1957: *Painting in Am.*
—1962: *Am. Paintings and Drawings from Mich. Coll.*
—1966: *Treasures from DIA*
Dunlap 1834: W. Dunlap *Hist. of Rise and Progress of Arts of Design in U. S.* New York (illus. repr. Boston 1918)
Eisen 1932: G. Eisen *Portr. of Washington* New York
Eliot 1957: A. Eliot *300 Years of Am. Painting* New York
Ewers 1965: J. Ewers *Artists of the Old West* Garden City
Ferargil 1945: *Early Am. Paintings* New York, Gall.
Fielding 1926: M. Fielding *Dict. of Am. Painters etc.* Phila.
Fink 1964: *A. Jay Fink Coll. of Min.* WAG
Fleischman 1960: *Am. Painting 1760-1960* Milwaukee Art Cen.
—1964: *Am. Painting 1765-1963* Tucson, Univ. of Ariz. Art Gall.
Flexner 1939: J. Flexner *America's Old Masters* New York
—1947: *First Flowers of Our Wilderness* Boston
—1950: *Short Hist. of Am. Painting* Boston
—1954: *Light of Distant Skies* New York
—1957: *Pocket Hist. of Am. Painting* New York
—1962: *That Wilder Image* New York
Frankenstein 1953: A. Frankenstein *After the Hunt* Berkeley
Gabriel 1926: R. Gabriel *Toilers of Land and Sea* New Haven
—1929: *Lure of the Frontier* New Haven
Geske 1953: N. Geske *Rembrandt Peale* (M. A. thesis New York Univ.)
Girl Scouts 1929: *Nat. Council of Girl Scouts Loan Exh.* New York
Green 1966: S. Green *Am. Art* New York
Greensburg 1959: *250 Years of Art in Penn.* Westmoreland Co. Mus. of Art
Groce and Wallace 1957: G. Groce and D. Wallace *NYHS Dict. of Artists in Am. 1564-1860* New Haven
Hagerstown 1955: *Portr. from Coll. of NGA* (Md.) Washington Co. MFA
Halsey 1925: R. Halsey *Homes of Our Ancestors* Garden City
Hart 1897: C. Hart "Life Portr. of Geo. Washington" *McClure's Mag.* Feb. 1897
—1904: *Cat. of Engr. Portr. of Washington* New York
—1915: *CWP Allegory of Wm. Pitt* Boston
Hartford 1935: *3 Cent. of Am. Painting & Sculpture* (Conn.) Wadsworth Atheneum
—1938: *Painters of Still Life*
—1942: *In Memoriam*
—25: *25 Am. Paintings*
—1963: *Harvest of Plenty*
—1964: *Let There Be Light*
Henderson 1911: H. Henderson *PAFA and Other Coll. of Phila.* Boston
HSP 1872: *Cat. of Paintings etc.*

—1942: *Cat. of Paintings and Min.*
Huyghe 1964: R. Huyghe (ed.) *Larousse Ency. of Ren. and Baroque Art* New York
IBM 1966: *Min. in NCFA* New York, Gall.
Illinois 1966: *19th Cent. Am. Artists* Ill. Arts Council exh. to Springfield, Peoria, and Davenport, Iowa
Isham 1905, 1927: S. Isham *Hist. of Am. Painting* New York
Jackman 1928: R. Jackman *Am. Arts* Chicago
Jackson 1938: E. Jackson *Silhouette* New York
Janson 1957: H. and D. Janson *Picture Hist. of Painting* New York
Jensen 1955: O. Jensen "Peales" *Am. Heritage* Apr.
Johnston 1882: E. Johnston *Original Portr. of Washington* Boston
Kansas City 1949: *W. R. Nelson Coll.* (Mo.) Nelson Gall.
—1953: *Am. Ancestor Portr.*
Karolik 1949: *M. and M. Karolik Coll. of Am. Paintings 1815-65* Boston MFA
—1962: *M. & M. Karolik Coll. of Am. Water Colors & Drawings 1800-75*
Knoedler 1945: *Navy Exh.* New York, Gall.
—1954: *Am. Panorama*
—1958: *Am. Portr. 1755-1815*
LaFollette 1929: S. LaFollette *Art in Am.* New York
Larkin 1949, 1960: O. Larkin *Art and Life in Am.* New York
Lee 1929: C. Lee *Early Am. Portr. Painters* New Haven
Levy 1941: *Mary H. Sully Coll. of Am. Paintings* New York, Gall.
Lewis 1875: *Lewis Art Gall., Coldwater, Mich.*
Lewis 1934: *John F. Lewis Coll. of Am. Portr.* PAFA
London 1946: *Am. Painting* Tate Gall.
Lossing 1871: B. Lossing *Home of Washington* Hartford, Conn.
Loubat 1878: J. Loubat *Medallic Hist. of U. S. of Am.* New York
Louisville 1947: *Colonial and Later Am. Portr. and Silver* Speed Art Mus.
—1949: *Ky. Portr. Gall.*
—1960: *14 Seasons of Art Accessions*
—1961: *Exh. Jr. Art Gall.*
Lyon 1941: *Bundles for Britain Benefit Exh.* New York, Gall.
Madison 1952: *Exh.* (Wisc.) Art Assoc.
Mather 1927: F. Mather et al. *Am. Spirit in Art* New Haven
Mendelowitz 1960: D. Mendelowitz *Hist. of Am. Art* New York
MHS 1945: *Handlist of Min.*
Milwaukee 1956: *Still Life Painting Since 1470* Art Inst. and Cincinnati Art Mus.
—1966: *Inner Circle* Art Cen.
Minneapolis 1963: *4 Cent. of Am. Art* Inst. of Arts
MMA 1927: *Min. Painted in Am. 1720-1850*
—1936: *Benj. Franklin and His Circle*
—1939: *Life in Am.*
—1948: *Your Navy*
—1963: *Am. Art from Am. Coll.*
—1965: *Am. Paintings* (cat. v. 1)

MOMA 1943: *Am. Realists and Magic Realists*

Monro 1948: I. and K. Monro: *Index to Repro. of Am. Paintings* New York (1st supp. 1964)

Morgan and Fielding 1931: J. Morgan and M. Fielding *Life Portr. of Washington* Lancaster, Pa.

NAD—: *Exh. Record* NYHS 1943

—1942: *Our Heritage*

Newark 1958: *Nature's Bounty and Man's Delight* Mus.

—1959: *Survey: 50 Years*

—1965: *Women Artists of Am.*

New Haven 1940: *Early Am. Min.* YUAG

New London 1944: *Trumbull and His Contemporaries* (Conn.) Lyman Allyn Mus.

—1960: *Am. and European Drawings, Paintings and Watercolors*

New York 1940: *Masterpieces of Art* World's Fair

—1941: *Philip Hone's New York* Mus. of City

NYHS 1941: *Cat. of Am. Portr.*

—1948: *Up from the Cradle*

Oberlin 1946: "Arts in Am. in 18th Cent." (Ohio) Allen Mem. Art Mus. *Bull.* May

Ogg 1927: F. Ogg *Builders of Republic* New Haven

PAFA—: *Exh. Record* APS 1955

—1902: *Descr. Cat. of Perm. Coll.*

Paris 1938: *Trois siecles d'art aux Etats-Unis* Mus. Nat.

Peale 1923: *Portr. by CWP and James Peale and Rembrandt Peale* PAFA (final ed.)

—1937: *Paintings by Rembrandt Peale* BPM

—1939: *James Peale & His Family* New York, Walker Gall.

—1941: *Am. Paintings by CWP et al.* New York, J. Graham & Sons (cf. BPM)

—1944: *Paintings and Watercolors by Peale Family* Phil., McClees Gall.

—1953: *Paintings by Members of Peale Family* New York, Century Assoc.

—1954: *Paintings by Peale Family* Cincinnati Art Mus.

—1959: *Raphaelle Peale* Milwaukee Art Cen. and New York, Knoedler Gall.

—1960: "Fabulous Peale Family" *Kennedy Qu.* June (New York)

—1963: *Peale Heritage 1763-1963* Hagerstown, Md., Washington Co. MFA (corr. ed.)

—1965: *Peale Family and PBM* BPM

Penn. 1955: *Penn. Painters* Univ. Park, State Univ.

Phila. 1795: *Exh. of Columbianum or Am. Acad. of Painting etc.*

—1811: *Appolodorian Gall.*

—1887: *Hist. Portr.* PAFA

—1940: *Life in Phila.* Mus. of Art

—1944: *Star Presentation* PAFA

—1951: *Golden Jubilee Exh. of Min.*

—1955: *150th Anniv.*

—1956: *250th Anniv. of Birth of Benj. Franklin* APS

Pierson 1960: W. Pierson and M. Davidson *Arts of U. S.* New York

Pittsburgh 1925: *Early Am. Portr.* Carnegie Inst.

—1940: *Survey of Am. Painting*

Poesch 1957: J. Poesch "Germantown Landscapes" *Antiques* Nov.

—1961: *Titian R. Peale and His Journals of Wilkes Expedition* Phila.

Pratt 1917: *Coll. of Herbert L. Pratt* New York

—1946: *Herbert L. Pratt Coll.* Amherst

Providence 1954: *Am. Painters of Precise Vision* R. I. Sch. of Design Mus. of Art

Raleigh 1945: *Am. Scene from 1750* N.C. State Art Soc.

—1963: *Carolina Charter Tercentenary* N.C. Mus. of Art

Richardson 1944: E. Richardson *Am. Romantic Painting* New York

—1956: *Painting in Am.* New York

Richmond 1929: *Vir. Hist. Portr. 1585-1830* Vir. House

—1947: *Portr. Panorama* Vir. MFA

Ringel 1932: F. Ringel *Am. as Am. See It* New York

Robb 1951: D. Robb *Harper Hist. of Painting* New York

Rochester 1965: *In Focus* (N.Y.) Mem. Art Gall.

Roos 1954: F. Roos *Illus. Handbook of Art Hist.* New York

Rousuck 1947: *Portr. of Geo. Washington* New York, Scott & Fowles

Saginaw 1948: *Am. Painting* (Mich.) Mus.

St.-Gaudens 1941: H. St.-Gaudens *Am. Artist and His Times* New York

St. Louis 1964: *200 Years of Am. Painting* City Art Mus.

St. Petersburg 1965: *Inaugaural Exh.* (Fla.) MFA

San Francisco 1915: *Off. Cat. of Dept. of Fine Arts* Internat. Expo.

—1935: *Am. Painting* M. H. de Young Mem. Mus.

—1939: *Hist. Am. Paintings* Internat. Expo.

—1949: *Illusionism & Trompe l'Oeil* Cal. Pal. of Legion of Honor

—1950: *Illus. of Selected Works* M. H. de Young Mem. Mus.

Santa Barbara 1941: *Painting Today and Yesterday* Mus. of Art

—1958: *Fruits and Flowers in Painting*

—1961: *200 Years of Am. Painting*

—1966: *Am. Portr. in Cal. Coll.*

Sarasota 1949: *Am. Painting: 3 Cent.* Ringling Mus. of Art

Schenectady 1960: *Survey of Am. Art* (N.Y.) Union College

Sellers 1933: H. Sellers "Engr. by CWP" *Penn. Mag. of Hist. and Biog.* Apr.

—1939: C. Sellers *Artist of Revolution: Early Life of CWP* Hebron, Conn.

—1947: *CWP: Later Life 1790-1827* Phila. (above repr. as v. 1)

—1952: *Portr. and Min. by CWP* Phila. (cited as Sellers no.)

—1962: *Benj. Franklin in Portr.* New Haven

Sherman 1932: F. Sherman *Early Am. Painting* New York

Shoolman 1942: R. Shoolman and C. Slatkin *Enjoyment of Art in Am.* Phila.

Slatkin 1947: C. Slatkin and R. Shoolman *Treasury of Am.*

Drawings New York

Soby 1935: J. Soby *After Picasso* New York

Springfield 1935: *30 Paintings of Early Am.* (Mass.) MFA

Stauffer 1907: D. Stauffer *Am. Engr. upon Copper and Steel* New York

Sterling 1952: C. Sterling *Nature Morte* Paris

Stoudt 1964: J. Stoudt *Early Penn. Arts and Crafts* New York

Taft 1938: R. Taft *Photography and Am. Scene* New York

Taylor 1954: F. Taylor *50 Cent. of Art* New York

Tuckerman 1867: H. Tuckerman *Book of Artists* New York

Tucson 1964: *Bird in Art* Tucson, Univ. of Ariz. Art Gall.

Union 1921: *Early Am. Portr. Painters* N.Y., Union League Club

—1922: *Portr. of Early Am. Artists*

UP 1965: *Univ. Prints Complete Cat.* Cambridge, Mass.

Upjohn 1963: E. Upjohn and J. Sedgwick *Highlights Illus. Hist. of Art* New York

Vancouver 1955: *200 Years of Am. Painting* Art Gall.

Walker 1913: *Descr. Cat. of Thos. B. Walker Art Coll.* Minneapolis

—1927: *Walker Art Gall.* Minneapolis

—1951: J. Walker *Paintings from Am.* Baltimore

Walker and James 1943: J. Walker and M. James *Great Am. Paintings* New York

Washington 1925: *Early Am. Paintings, Min. and Silver* NGA

—1932: *Geo. Washington Bicentennial* (D.C.) Corcoran Gall. of Art

—1937: *U. S. Constitution Sesquicentennial Portr. Exh.*

—1950: *Am. Processional 1492-1900*

—1959: *Am. Muse*

—1960: *Am. Painters of South*

—1966: *Cat. of Coll. of Am. Paintings*

Wehle 1927: H. Wehle and T. Bolton *Am. Min. 1730-1850* N.Y.

Wharton 1898: A. Wharton *Heirlooms in Min.* Phila.

White 1965: *Am. Min. Exh.* Washington, D.C., Adams, Davidson & Co.

Whitney 1954: *Am. Painting in 19th Cent.* New York, Mus. of Am. Art

—1966: *Art of U. S. 1670-1966*

Wildenstein 1953: *Landmarks in Am. Art* New York, Gall.

—1957: *Am. Vision*

—1959: *Masterpieces of Corcoran Gall. of Art*

Wilmington 1962: *Am. Painting 1857-69* Del. Art Cen.

Wood 1927: W. Wood and R. Gabriel *Winning of Freedom* New Haven

Worcester 1922: *Cat. of Paintings and Drawings* (Mass.) Art Mus.

Yale 1951: *Yale Univ. Portr. Index* 1701-1951 New Haven

4 (detail)

4 (detail)

INDEX OF PORTRAITS

Catalog (not page) numbers are given. Persons noticed as having posed for works other than portraits are included, as are artists whose works are catalogued. Parentheses enclose catalog numbers of works *by* artists. Persons listed in the Abbreviated Genealogy are not indexed *per se* but their genealogy numbers are given in square brackets when they do appear here. An asterisk (*) signifies inclusion in *(Concise) Dictionary of American Biography* or *Webster's Biographical Dictionary* or both.

PEALE PORTRAITS OF WASHINGTON: A NOTE

PRESIDENT WASHINGTON (1795), canvas 29 x 23¾ by C. W. Peale (cf. no. 56). *The New-York Historical Society* (not in the exhibition)

The myth that Charles Willson Peale painted fourteen life portraits of Washington originated with Rembrandt Peale, and was followed by Theodore Bolton and Harry L. Binsse in *Antiquarian* (Feb. 1931). As early as 1897 Charles H. Hart in *McClure's Magazine* (Feb. 1897) implied that Charles Willson Peale's portraits of Washington fell into seven distinct types (not counting silhouettes). Charles Coleman Sellers (1952) identifies only the following seven life portraits (his number is given; the number of replicas may be deduced by interpolation, the last being 949):

1 (894) Signed and dated 1772. Canvas 50½ x 41½. Three-quarter length. Washington and Lee University

2 (896) 1776. Canvas 43½ x 37½. Three-quarter length. Brooklyn Museum

3 (899) 1777. Miniature 1½ x 1¼. Metropolitan Museum of Art

4 (904) 1779. Canvas 94 x 59. Full length. Pennsylvania Academy of the Fine Arts

5 (933) Signed and dated 1784. Canvas 94½ x 57½. Full length. Princeton University

6 (939) 1787. Canvas 23¾ x 19. Bust. Pennsylvania Academy of the Fine Arts.

7 (942) 1795. Canvas 29 x 23¾. Half length. New-York Historical Society

In the card catalog of photographs at the Frick Art Reference Library, New York, which probably houses the most extensive classified collection of photographs of American paintings, there are the following number of portraits of Washington by or attributed to the Peales:

Charles Willson Peale 40 (Sellers lists 56)
Harriet Cany Peale 1 (after Rembrandt)
James Peale 17 (including 2 miniatures)
Mary Jane Peale (after Rembrandt)
Raphaelle Peale 1 (watercolor)
Rembrandt Peale 61 (including portholes and copies after other artists; Rembrandt said he did 80 portholes)
Charles Peale Polk 29

NOTE
Paintings to be shown at Detroit only: no. 10, 139, 167